AN INTRODUCTION TO PIC MICROCONTROLLERS

Other Titles of Interest

AN INTRODUCTION TO PIC MICROCONTROLLERS

by

R. A. PENFOLD

BERNARD BABANI (publishing) LTD
THE GRAMPIANS
SHEPHERDS BUSH ROAD
LONDON W6 7NF
ENGLAND

Please Note

Although every care has been taken with the production of this book to ensure that any projects, designs, modifications and/or programs, etc., contained herewith, operate in a correct and safe manner and also that any components specified are normally available in Great Britain, the Publishers do not accept responsibility in any way for the failure, including fault in design, of any project, design, modification or program to work correctly or to cause damage to any other equipment that it may be connected to or used in conjunction with, or in respect of any other damage or injury that may be so caused, or do the Publishers accept responsibility in any way for the failure to obtain specified components.

Notice is also given that if equipment that is still under warranty is modified in any way or used or connected with home-built equipment then that warranty may be void.

© 1997 BERNARD BABANI (publishing) LTD

First Published – October 1997
Reprinted – April 2000
Reprinted – June 2001
Reprinted – June 2003

British Library Cataloguing in Publication Data

A catalogue record for this book is available from the British Library

ISBN 0 85934 394 4

Cover designed by George Arthur
Printed and bound in Great Britain by Antony Rowe Ltd, Chippenham, Wiltshire

Preface

You could be forgiven for thinking that the microcontroller was a very recent invention, but they have in fact been in existence for many years now. However, it is only relatively recently that microcontrollers have become available at very low prices. This makes them suitable for many applications where they would have previously represented an expensive solution, and has resulted in an explosion in their popularity. The early microcontrollers were basically just slightly stripped down versions of the eight-bit microprocessors of the period, with some built-in ROM, RAM, and input/output ports. Modern microcontrollers are mostly designed as such from scratch, or have evolved so far from their origins that they are effectively purpose designed chips. This makes it relatively easy to write the software, especially with the microcontrollers of the RISC (reduced instruction set computer) variety.

The PIC series of microcontrollers seem to be the most popular at present, and they have proven their ability to perform well in a wide range of applications. They are quite inexpensive, which means that they often have a cost advantage over circuits based on conventional logic integrated circuits. PIC based projects lend themselves to miniaturisation as in most cases very little discrete circuitry is required. PIC microcontrollers are constructed using CMOS technology and they have the low levels of power consumption associated with CMOS logic devices. Consequently, they can be used in applications where small battery powered equipment is required.

Although PIC microcontrollers are reasonably straight-forward to use, designing a project based on a microcontroller is obviously very different to designing a conventional equivalent. Even if you have some experience of computer programming and electronic circuit design, producing projects based on PIC processors could prove to be difficult at first. The main difficulty is that the programming is done at a very low level using assembly language. In order to undertake programming at this level you need to have a reasonable knowledge of what the processor does, and the registers it contains. Fortunately, the

PIC register and instruction sets are both quite simple, and armed with a knowledge of both, plus some basic microcontroller techniques, it is not too difficult to start producing simple PIC based gadgets.

This book guides you through the basics of PIC programming, including details of the register set, numbering systems, the PIC instruction set, using the analogue to digital converter, etc. The final chapter provides some simple demonstration programs and circuits that you can experiment with. No previous experience of microcontrollers or programming is assumed, but you will, of course, need some electronics know-how in order to design PIC based systems.

R. A. Penfold

Contents

Chapter 1

MICROPROCESSOR BASICS

A PIC microcontroller is virtually a complete computer on a single chip. Admittedly it is a fairly basic computer in comparison to the average PC, but for many purposes, such as measurement and control applications, the power of even a fairly modest PC is slightly 'over the top'. Although a PIC microcontroller has limited computing power by normal standards, it is more than adequate for a vast range of useful applications. It is easy to underestimate the computing power of a PIC processor, and it has to be borne in mind that all the chips in the PIC series are RISC (reduced instruction set computer) processors. Basically all this means is that they have a very limited range of instructions (about 35 in the case of PIC processors), but each instruction is completed very efficiently. In fact a RISC processor normally completes most instructions in just one clock cycle. As some PIC processors can handle 20 million clock pulses a second, this obviously enables tasks to be carried out at a very high rate. In fact it is often necessary to slow down the processor by using a reduced clock frequency or by adding timing loops into the program. Operating speed is also aided by having instructions that are well matched to the likely applications of PIC processors. There are no instructions for floating point calculations, but a PIC processor is not intended for applications that involve any advanced mathematics. The PIC devices are simple but streamlined processors that are specifically intended for general control and measurement applications, and they work very well when used for suitable tasks.

The Microprocessor

Although a computer is extremely complex, its basic function is fairly simple. The block diagram of Figure 1.1 shows the basic arrangement used in a computer. Regardless of its function, a computer does nothing more than take in data on its inputs, process the data in some way, and then send the data to

1

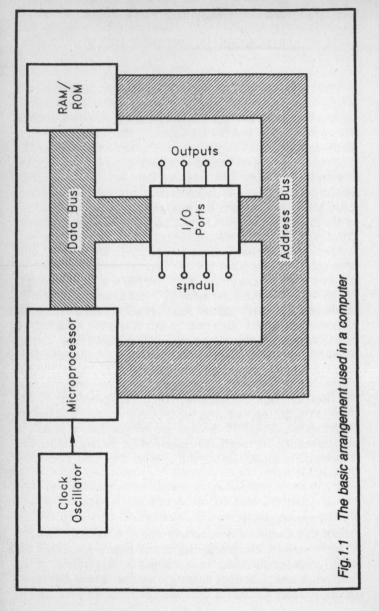

Fig.1.1   The basic arrangement used in a computer

its outputs. As a simple example, a word processor takes data typed into the keyboard, and stores it in memory. In this example the computer is not doing any mathematical processing of the data, but it does enable the data to be edited via further input from a keyboard. This can be in the form of material added into the existing data, material being deleted, or practically any required change. It is just a matter of having the system alter the data in memory to give the required change to the material. The data entered into the system is output to a monitor so that the user can check that everything is as required, and once a piece has been perfected it is sent to the printer via another set of outputs.

The microprocessor is at the centre of the computer, and in a sense it controls everything else. However, the microprocessor itself is actually controlled via a program which is stored in the computer's memory. This memory is in the form of random access memory (RAM) and read only memory (ROM). The difference between the two is that ROM retains its contents when the computer is switched off, whereas RAM only retains its contents while the computer is turned on. Although the names suggest that the data in RAM can be accessed randomly whereas the data in ROM can not, with both types it is possible to access any memory location whenever required. In a normal computer system the ROM stores a simple program that gets the system under way when it is switched on. The application program (word processor, spreadsheet, or whatever) is then loaded into RAM and run. Some of the RAM is set aside for use by the program to store data entered by the user, or whenever large amounts of data must be put into temporary storage.

A PIC processor does not handle things in quite the same way, and the program that gets the computer under way and the main program are one and the same. The program is therefore stored in ROM, and the RAM is only used for temporary data storage. One reason for this method of working is that the amount of RAM contained in the processor is strictly limited. Loading large and complex programs into RAM is simply not an option. However, the main reason is that PIC systems are dedicated to a single function, and they do not operate on the basis of having a general hardware which is made to perform the required function by loading suitable software. If you require three different functions it is necessary to have a separate PIC based system to handle each one.

This may seem to be a bit extravagant, but it has to be remembered that each PIC based system is quite inexpensive. Also, in typical PIC applications you require easy to use items of equipment that you simply switch on and they start to operate immediately. You do not really want the bother of loading programs from disc, or the added size, weight, and cost that would result from adding a disc drive to the system. With microcontroller based systems it is not usually apparent to the user that they are dealing with a form of computer based equipment. By normal computing standards the amount of storage space for your programs is tiny, but PIC processors are not normally used to perform highly complex tasks. Even so, it is sometimes necessary to write efficient software if it is to fit into the ROM.

The microprocessor communicates with the memory circuits via the data bus, which has eight wires in the case of PIC processors. A collection of connecting wires is known as a bus, and PIC processors have an eight bit bus. The data bus is bi-directional, which simply means that it is used both when the microprocessor is writing data to the memory circuits and when it is reading data from them. This bus is also used when reading data from or writing it to external hardware via the input and output ports. The required memory location or input/output port is selected via another bus which is called the address bus. In the case of PIC processors this bus is 9 to 12 wires (bits) wide, depending on the amount of memory the chip contains. The address bus is not bi-directional, and it is a set of outputs on the microprocessor, and inputs on the memory and input/output circuits.

The program in ROM controls the microprocessor, but it is the microprocessor itself that generates the signals which control the rest of the hardware and ensure everything happens in the right order. The necessary signals are carried via a collection of wires that are called the control bus, but this is not really a bus in the same sense as the address and data buses. The control bus carries what are really individual signals and not a set of signals that operate together in quite the same way as those in the address and data buses. The main function of the control bus is to ensure that the memory and input/output circuits read from and place data onto the data bus at the correct times. Having a bi-directional data bus simplifies the circuit in many ways, but the timing of read and write operations is obviously critical. The system will crash if the microprocessor and a peripheral circuit try to place data on to the data bus simultaneously, and it is also possible that the hardware could be damaged. Having the microprocessor in control of this function ensures that conflicts on the data bus should never occur. The control bus is not included in Figure 1.1 for the sake of clarity, but it is clearly an essential part of the system. An advantage of using a microcontroller is that the buses are an internal part of the device, and are not externally accessible. Therefore, this is an aspect of the hardware that PIC system designers do not have to bother about.

The microprocessor flows from one instruction to the next at a rate which is controlled by the clock oscillator, which is often referred to simply as the 'clock'. All this circuit does is to provide a regular stream of electrical pulses at a rate that is normally a few million pulses per second. One of the peculiarities of PIC processors is that they can operate with a very wide range of clock frequencies. With a normal microprocessors it is only possible to use a fairly restricted range of clock rates as anything outside this range does not provide suitable bus timing. There can also be problems with the memory getting a severe case of amnesia. The acceptable range of clock frequencies varies from one PIC processor to another, but in some cases there is no lower limit. Although there seems to be a never ending quest for higher and higher clock rates in the world of computing, not all applications require a very high operating speed. With a normal microprocessor it is often necessary to slow things down by inserting lots of timing loops in the software to provide delays. In some cases PIC processors offer the simple alternative of using a very low clock frequency. However, note that this method is only practical in applications where the processor never needs to operate at high speed. In theory it is possible to stop the clock and start it again without crashing the system! When I tried this with a simple PIC based circuit the short rest when the clock was stopped did not prevent the unit from

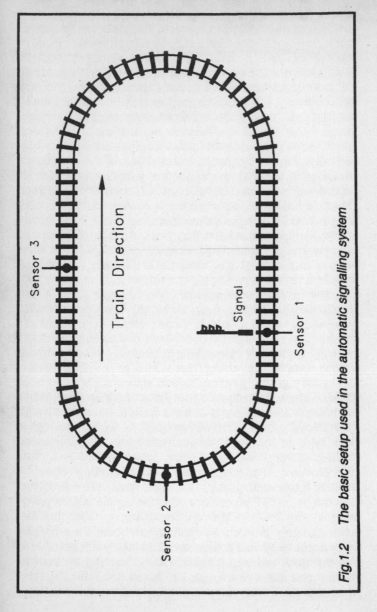

Fig.1.2   The basic setup used in the automatic signalling system

functioning properly when the clock was restarted. This is certainly not possible with most other microprocessors.

Seeing the Light

So how would a microprocessor based system handle a simple task such as controlling an automatic three-colour signal for a model railway? Figure 1.2 shows a general scheme of things, with three tracks sensors in addition to the signal. The basic idea is for the signal to change to red when the train passes sensor one, which is positioned right next to the signal. When the train passes sensor two, which is positioned further down the track, the signal changes to amber. Finally, when the train passes sensor three the signal is sent back to green once again. This is basically the same system that is used on 'the real thing', and it ensures that there is always a reasonable distance from one train to the next.

In our model train example the signal would contain three LEDs or miniature bulbs that would be controlled by three outputs of the microcontroller. The three sensors would be something fairly basic such as micro-switches or reed switches that would close momentarily as the model train passed by. For the sake of this example we will assume that sensors one, two, and three are read by input lines one, two, and three of the microcontroller. Similarly, we will assume that the green, red, and amber signal lights are controlled by outputs one to three respectively.

Logic outputs only have two valid states which are logic 0 ('low') and logic 1 ('high'), and logic inputs only recognise these two states. The two logic levels are respectively represented by a low voltage of around two volts or less, and a higher voltage of about three to five volts. It is from this that their alternative 'low' and 'high' names are derived. The program in the microcontroller would initially set the signal to green by placing output one high, and the other two inputs low. Actually, the hardware could be designed to operate the other way round with a low logic level switching on a light, but it is generally better if things are done the obvious way, which in this case means having a high level to switch on a light.

The program would then monitor the three sensor switches at a high rate so that there would be no risk of a change in state being missed. Eventually the train would reach and operate sensor one. Again, the hardware could be designed to provide either a high or a low logic level when a sensor switch is operated. Doing things the obvious way makes life easier, and it would therefore be sensible to have each switch generate a high logic state when it is activated. The program would therefore keep testing the sensor switches until it receives a high logic state from one of them. If everything goes according to plan it will be sensor one that is activated first. The program then sets output one low to switch off the green light, and sets output two high to turn on the red light. The testing of the sensor switches then continues until sensor two is activated. The program then switches off the red light by setting output two low, and the amber light would be activated by setting output three high. The testing process would then continue again until a signal from sensor three was detected. The green light would then be turned on by setting output one high, and the amber light would be switched off by setting output three low. This takes the system back to its initial state, and it would then repeat this whole process indefinitely as the train went around the track.

A simple set-up of this type is really under-utilizing the capabilities of a microcontroller, but it demonstrates the basic way in which a microcontroller can be applied to a practical application. A signalling system based on a microcontroller would be quite capable of controlling several signals, together with added complications such as direction sensors and four-state signals. The limits are often those of the designer's imagination and programming skills rather than those of the microcontroller.

Keeping Count

When a microcontroller is first switched on it goes through a resetting and initialisation process that ensures everything is set up and working correctly before the first instruction is fetched from memory and run. A certain address is used for the start of the program, and the address bus is initially set to the appropriate pattern of logic levels for this particular memory location. The first instruction is then fetched from memory and executed. The next clock pulse increments a counter within the microprocessor (the program counter or PC), and this moves the address bus on to the next memory location.

The next instruction is then fetched from this memory location, and performed. The program could just continue in this fashion, going sequentially through all the instructions one by one until they had all been completed. This is a bit limiting though, and is not the way things operate in practice. One problem is that the processor would rapidly run out of instructions and grind to a halt. Practical applications require the system to go on functioning indefinitely.

Practical programs make use of loops, jumps, and branches, which take the program out of its normal straightforward sequential scheme of things. The most simple form of loop is where the program simply goes back to the beginning once the final instruction has been performed. This is a feature of most programs, and is the most simple means of keeping the system running indefinitely. Loops, branches, etc., are considered in more detail later on.

In the Flow

When working out even the most simple of programs it is generally a good idea to start with a simple chart or diagram which goes through the program step-by-step. A diagram of this type is called a flow chart, and there is a standard set of symbols for this type of chart (Figure 1.3). Few programmers seem to adopt standard flow charts, and most seem to use charts of their own style. In fact many programmers seem to use what would be more accurately described as a flow list or flow table rather than a chart. My own preference is for a list of program steps with lines to show how the program branches in and out of the main flow. The precise form of the chart, list, or table is not really that important. Provided it enables you to get everything clear in your mind so that it is easy to write the 'real thing', the chart (or whatever) will have served its purpose.

When working out a flow chart it is not necessary to get too technical, since its purpose is simply to provide you with a logical sequence of events that will provide the desired result. In our example of an automatic model train signal, it would not be necessary to deal in terms of actual input/output ports and the lines of these ports that would be used. Instead, it would just be a matter of working on the basis of what each program step would actually achieve. For instance, the first program step

9

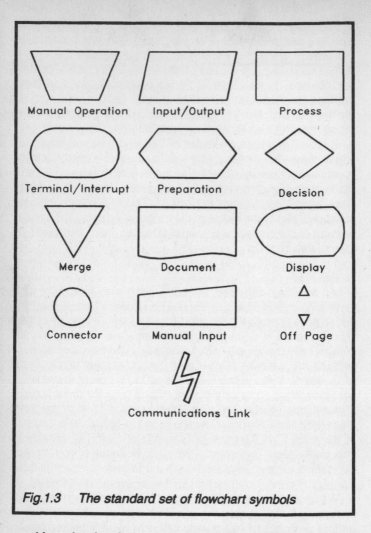

Fig.1.3   The standard set of flowchart symbols

would set the signal at green, and the first symbol in the chart would be marked accordingly. It would not be labelled something along the lines of 'set line three of port A high'. Once the initial chart has been completed you may wish to work out a more detailed version before writing the program code. It would certainly be necessary to at least make a few notes detailing the function of each input and output port, and where appropriate the function of each line of each port. Once again, programmers generally work out their own way of working, and the best method for one person is not necessarily well suited to anyone else.

Figure 1.4 shows a suggested flow chart for the automatic model train signal. Most programs start with some initial conditions being set and in this case the only thing to set at the outset is the state of the signal which is set to green. The next step is to read the sensor switches to determine whether or not any have been activated. The program then has to make a decision which is dependent on the results of reading the sensor switches. If a switch has not been activated the program must read the switches again and continue reading them until one has been operated. This is achieved by simply looping the program back to the instruction where the sensors are read. The program therefore loops around these two program instructions until a switch has been activated. It then breaks out of the loop and moves on to the next section. This looping process is an essential part of practically every program ever written, and even quite simple programs usually feature several loops. The same is true of decision making instructions of the 'if this condition is met then do this, else do that' variety. You need to be careful when writing loop routines as it only requires a minor oversight to get the program into a loop from which it can never break out!

Once a switch has been activated, the program moves on to the next section where it must make the appropriate alteration to the signal. This requires more decision making instructions, and there is more than one way of handling this sort of thing. In this case there are only three possible actions that the program can take, which are to set the signal to red, amber, or green. The most simple solution is probably to use a series of three decision making instructions, one for each possible outcome. The first of these instructions tests to see if sensor one was activated, and sets the signal to green if it was. The next two instructions are similar, but test sensors two and three, and set the signal to amber and green respectively if they detect that the switch has been activated. Once these three instructions have

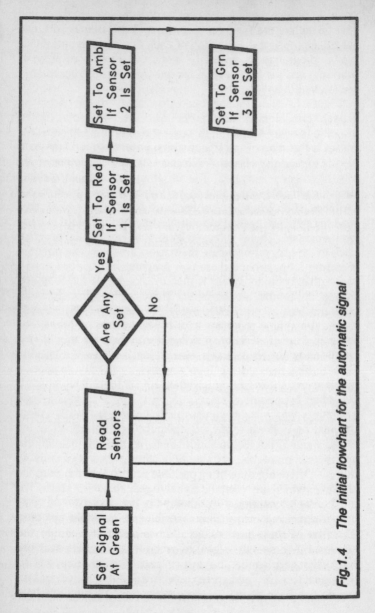

Fig.1.4　The initial flowchart for the automatic signal

been completed the signal must be at the correct state, and it is then a matter of looping back to the part of the program where the sensor switches are read. The program then continues to loop around these instructions once again until a sensor is activated. This whole process repeats for as long as power is applied to the system.

Refining

Once you have worked out a general form for a program it is necessary to make a detailed investigation to see whether you have overlooked or over simplified anything. In this example there are one or two questions to answer, and potential flaws that must be addressed. One question is where do the series of three decision making instructions obtain their data? One possibility is for each of these sections of the program to read the sensor switches, or to read the relevant sensor switch anyway. This is probably a viable way of handling the program in this case, but is not the usual way of handling things. The only thing that might prevent the program from working properly using this method would be if the sensor switch was only activated for a very short time. It would then be possible for the program to break out of the small loop, but for the series of three decision making instructions to leave the signal unaltered because the switch would have returned to its standby state before the program reached them. This is unlikely in practice because the program would execute very rapidly provided a high clock frequency was used. However, this possibility can be avoided by placing the data initially read from the switches in RAM. The series of three decision making instructions can then operate on this data rather than reading the sensor switches again. This ensures that the signal must be set to the correct state even if the sensor switch has returned to the standby state.

A more likely cause of problems is the program executing too rapidly so that the active sensor switch is still active when the program loops back to the point where the switches are read again. In this particular case the program should still function properly if this should happen because it does not matter if the program keeps executing the three decision making instructions. It would simply result in the signal being

13

repeatedly set to the new state, which would mean in practice that it would remain in the correct state. In some applications though, this sort of unscheduled looping would cause problems and would have to be avoided. In this example it could be eliminated by including a time delay between the final decision making instruction and the loop back to where the sensors are read. Short delays are easily added using dummy instructions that do not actually achieve anything other than wasting time. Longer delays can be produced using a form of loop routine.

With many types of programming, the faster the program runs the better. The same is not always true of the software for control and measurement applications. It is often essential that the program operates in unison with hardware in the outside world. Sometimes this is achieved via signals passed to-and-fro between the processor and the external hardware, which is a system known as 'handshaking'. On other occasions the synchronisation is achieved by using delaying routines as and where necessary. This second method is more easily implemented, but it will not always provide adequate timing accuracy. Handshaking is generally the more reliable method. In applications where timing is critical it is essential to know how long certain sections of the program take to execute. Fortunately, this is easily calculated provided the duration of each clock cycle is known. It is just a matter of adding the total number of clock cycles that a routine will take, and then multiplying this by the duration of one clock cycle. Where good timing accuracy is essential it is normally necessary to use a crystal controlled clock oscillator.

One Step at a Time

When writing computer software you have to bear in mind that the microprocessor operates in what are really very simple steps. This is especially the case with a RISC processor such as a PIC type. When producing an initial flow chart it does not matter too much if each section of the chart actually involves more than one processor instruction. You may also have to modify the way in which the program operates in order to suit the instructions that are available. At some stage though, things have to be worked out in greater detail, and in a fashion that can actually be implemented by the processor. You may prefer to

14

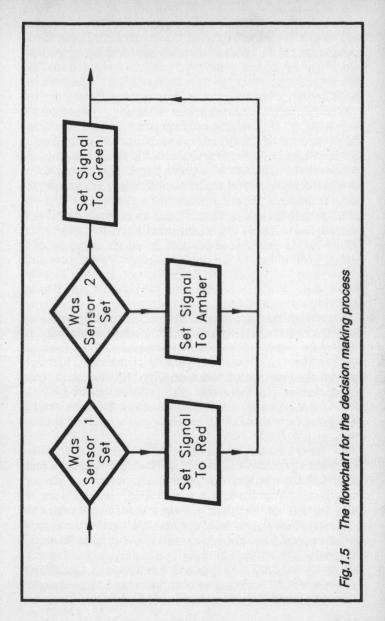

Fig.1.5   The flowchart for the decision making process

15

leave this until you start writing the program code, or you may like to produce a more detailed flow chart first. In our model signal example the series of three decision making instructions would almost certainly have to consist of more than three processor instructions. The flow chart of Figure 1.5 shows one possible way of handling the decision making process.

The first instruction determines whether or not sensor one was activated. If it was, the program sets the signal to red, and then jumps forward to the end of the routine. Programs usually contain numerous jump instructions which enable parts of the program to be bypassed. A loop uses a form of jump instruction to move backwards and repeat an action, but in this case the jump is forwards to avoid actions we do not require. This type of instruction is called a 'skip'. If sensor one was not activated, the program moves on to a second decision making stage where sensor two is tested. If sensor two is set, the signal is set to amber, but if it was not activated it must have been sensor three that was set. In this case the signal is set to green. In either event, once the signal has been set the program jumps to the end of this routine.

Even with this new improved decision making routine it is possible that five stages in the flow chart would translate into more than five processor instructions. This does not really matter though, and the purpose of the flow chart is to provide the programmer with a sensible basis for the program rather than to provide a sort of pseudo programming code. Provided the general scheme of things in the flow chart is workable, there should be no difficulty in converting it into a working program.

On the other hand, do not expect to get everything right first time when you start programming. The first thing you learn when you begin programming is that microprocessors are very unforgiving. You have to get everything just right or the program will not run properly. Programs for measurement and control applications are often quite simple, but they also tend to be rather pernickety. You often need to have to consider what is happening almost literally from one nanosecond to the next. However, provided you proceed carefully and thoughtfully programs can be perfected with a minimum of 'fine-tuning'.

Although the system outlined in Figure 1.5 is in many ways

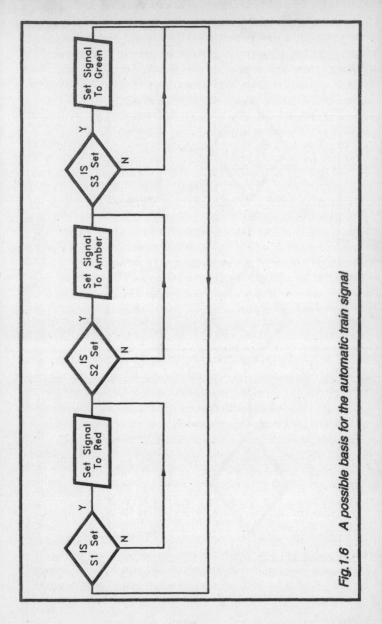

Fig.1.6   A possible basis for the automatic train signal

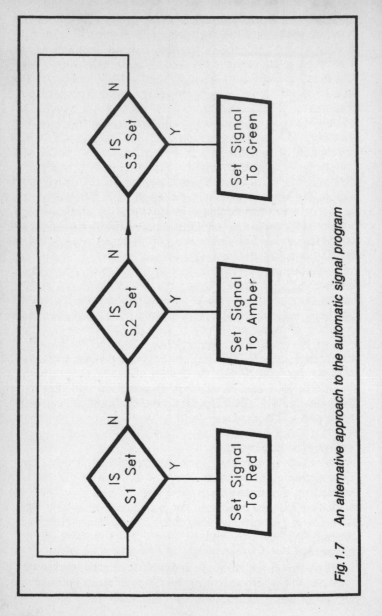

Fig.1.7 An alternative approach to the automatic signal program

sound, it has one major flaw. This is simply that it does not translate easily into PIC instructions. It is generally better to rework ideas to suit the instructions that are available rather than trying to put together convoluted routines that follow your initial scheme of things. The systems outlined in Figures 1.6 and 1.7 match up better with the actual instructions available. The method used in Figure 1.6 is to test to see if a particular switch has been set, and then jump one instruction ahead if it has not. The next instruction will set the signal to the appropriate state if the switch has been activated, but it will simply be skipped if it has not. The same basic procedure is repeated for all three switches. This method is delightfully simple, but in practice it only operates properly if the signal can be set to the desired state in a single instruction. With something as simple as controlling some LEDs there should be no problem in this single instruction limit, but in many applications this may be too limiting.

The alternative method of Figure 1.7 overcomes the single instruction limit. Again the sensor switches are tested one by one, but this time the program goes to a subroutine if a switch has been activated. There is a separate subroutine for each switch, and each subroutine sets the signal to the appropriate state for the switch that controls it. A subroutine is effectively a small program in its own right, and they are sometimes referred to as subprograms. Within the memory limits of the processor, the subroutines can be as long as you like, and they can undertake quite complex tasks if necessary. Subroutines form a major part of most software.

Software or Hardware

When designing a system based on a microcontroller there are often decisions to be made about how much of the task is handled by the processor and its program, and how much is tackled by external hardware. For example, if the system must drive seven segment displays, should these be controlled via external display decoders or direct from outputs of the microcontroller. The advantage of using external decoders is that it simplifies the software, and it also requires fewer output lines on the microcontroller. Using the microcontroller to provide the decoding simplifies the hardware and reduces cost, but it greatly increases the time needed to write the software. Also, remember that a microcontroller has limited storage space available for the program and does not have a vast number of input/output lines.

In some cases there may be no choice but to augment the microcontroller with some fairly sophisticated hardware. In fact a microcontroller is sometimes only a fairly minor part of the hardware, but it could still greatly reduce the overall cost and complexity of the system. Each case has to be considered on its own merits, and it often depends on how much time you are prepared to spend writing the software. As far as reasonably possible, it clearly makes sense to use the microcontroller to handle as much of the work as possible as this produces a neater and cheaper finished product.

Architecture

Microprocessors vary considerably in the way that they handle data, and in their internal arrangements (their 'architecture' as it is generally termed). The original microcontrollers were really just modified versions of the microprocessors of the day, and were far from ideal for many applications. They included facilities that were 'over the top' for most applications, and lacked some that would have been very useful. They were also very expensive in comparison to most of today's microcontrollers. Because of their expense and complexity, the early microcontrollers were really only suitable for the more advanced applications. For anything more straightforward it was usually cheaper and easier to use conventional logic circuits. Many of the more modern microcontrollers (including the PIC processors) are relatively simple and are a practical choice for anything but the most basic of applications. Internally they are either very basic or very streamlined, depending on your viewpoint. Although the streamlined approach may ultimately be a bit limiting, it does make it much easier to get started with your own simple microcontroller projects.

We will not consider the precise internal arrangements and functioning of PIC processors as this is something that you do not really need to understand in order to use them. On the other hand, when programming PIC processors you will not normally be using a high level language that almost totally shields you from the internal workings of the processor. You normally have to deal with the processor using a low level language that requires you to have some knowledge of how the processor handles instructions and data. Fortunately, a superficial knowledge of the internal goings on is all that is needed. At this stage we will settle for a brief look at the general way in which microcontrollers operate, but more specific information about PIC processors is provided in a later chapter.

A microcontroller contains a lot of complex logic circuitry which provides mathematical functions, and generally ensures that everything happens correctly. Although this circuitry is essential to the operation of the microcontroller, it is 'transparent' to the user. You program the processor with a series of instructions, and it carries them out. The exact way in which it decodes and executes the instructions is largely of academic importance, and the complexity of the internal circuits of microprocessors is such that this is probably just as well. All you really need is a basic knowledge of the parts of the processor that actually handle your data, and simply take for granted the circuits that operate in the background and perform the instructions.

The parts of the processor that you deal with first-hand are the registers. These store information, and the information that they contain can be overwritten and altered as frequently as required. In this respect the registers are much like RAM, and some of the registers in a microcontroller are effectively its RAM. Some of the registers have specific functions though, and are not simply used as general purpose data stores. Figure 1.8 shows the architecture for a simple microcontroller which demonstrates some of the fundamentals of microcontroller operation. The registers break down into two basic types, which are those in the memory map, and those which are an integral part of the microprocessor. With a conventional microprocessor there is a clear cut distinction between the two types, because the registers in the memory map are external to the microprocessor. These registers are accessed via an address placed on the address bus, and they are the RAM, ROM, and the input/output ports. Things are much the same with a

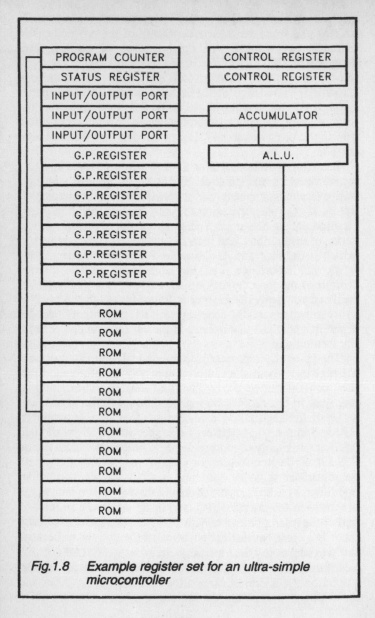

Fig. 1.8   Example register set for an ultra-simple microcontroller

microcontroller, but the RAM, ROM, and ports are integral rather than discrete. As already pointed out, the RAM is not used for program storage; the program is stored in the ROM. The RAM is used for general purpose data storage. Microprocessors have built-in registers that can be used as temporary data stores, but with microcontrollers the general purpose registers in the RAM are effectively merged. In a microcontroller context, the RAM is generally called the data registers, file registers, or something similar. The accepted term for PIC processors is file register (or register file, as you prefer).

With some microprocessors the input/output ports are placed in a separate map (the input/output map), and are accessed using a separate set of instructions. Most microcontrollers operate on the basis of having the ports in the memory map, and they are accessed using the same instructions that are used for memory accesses. This method is easier for the programmer, since it is only necessary to learn one type of instruction. On the other hand, you do have to keep in mind the addresses of the ports so that you do not inadvertently try to use them as ordinary registers.

Although there may appear to be no way of utilizing the registers that are not in the memory map, there are special instructions which enable them to be used. The most important of the extra registers is the accumulator, although it is not necessarily referred to by this name these days. The accumulator operates in conjunction with the arithmetic logic unit (ALU), which is the circuit that provides mathematical calculations such as addition and subtraction. The accumulator is very much at the centre of things, with virtually all data entering the accumulator at some stage. This can produce something of a bottleneck, and some microprocessors have two accumulators. Another approach is to enable the results of calculations or other processing of the data to be dumped straight into another register, so that the general purpose file registers can be used as pseudo accumulators. The PIC processors have some ability to do this.

The status register is another very important register. Conventionally this is not part of the memory map, but it is only fair to point out that with the PIC processors it is actually one of the memory mapped registers. Either way, it is used in much the same manner. The status register is used by the processor to store snippets of information which your programs can act on. Each piece of information is indicated by what is termed a 'status flag'. The most basic of these flags is the 'Z' (zero) flag, and this indicates whether or not the result of certain instructions is zero. This is commonly used in a loop which must complete a certain number of loops before the program moves on. Suppose that the program must loop 10 times. A value of 10 could be placed in the accumulator, and the loop routine could be made to subtract one from this value on each loop of the program. The status register is mainly used in conjunction with decision making instructions, and in this case such an instruction would be used to move out of the loop when the value in the accumulator reached zero, and the zero flag was set. This would, of course, occur after ten loops.

The Stack is used by the processor as a temporary store, and it is not necessarily directly accessible. In fact it is not directly accessible in the PIC processors, and you have to rely on the processors to use it correctly. Conventionally the Stack is a section of RAM that is used to store addresses and other data when the processor goes into some form of subroutine. As we have already seen, this is where the program breaks out of its normal flow and goes into what is normally a small program that is largely or totally separate from the main program. Having completed this subroutine, the processor goes back to where it left off, and continues from there as if nothing had happened. The information stored in the Stack enables the processor to be set with the same set of conditions that prevailed before the subroutine was performed.

A subroutine can be instigated by a program instruction, or via a piece of hardware driving an input of the microprocessor. This second method is known as an 'interrupt', and with a complex microprocessor system such as a PC there is a constant stream of interrupts. Practically every piece of hardware generates interrupts to indicate to the processor that it needs urgent attention. There is usually a hierarchy which ensures that more important devices take precedence over less important ones. In a PC the peripheral devices such as the mouse, keyboard, printer and serial ports, etc., all generate interrupts, and a fair percentage of the processor's time can be taken up servicing them all. By making these devices interrupt driven there is no risk of input from them being overlooked, with keyboard characters being missed for example. Microcontrollers generally make less use of subroutines and interrupts, and in the case of the PIC processors their capabilities are quite limited in this respect. In fact the more simple PIC processors do not implement interrupts at all. Hence a relatively simple Stack suffices.

If you have managed to follow things this far you should be starting to get the idea of the basic way in which a system based on a microcontroller functions. When the system is switched on it starts running the program instructions stored in ROM. Under the direction of the program, the processor reads data from input ports, provides any necessary processing, and places data on its outputs. This may seem a bit basic and of limited practical value, but this is the basic function of practically all logic circuits, whether they are based on a microprocessor, a microcontroller, or ordinary logic chips.

Microcontrollers are not suitable for all applications, but they are well suited to most logic oriented applications.

Points to Remember

A microcontroller is a complete computer contained in a single chip. It has built-in memory circuits for the program, and input/output ports to communicate with the outside world.

The basic function of a microcontroller is to take in data on its inputs, process it in some way, and place new data on its outputs.

A microcontroller, like any logic circuit, only deals with signals at logic levels. Logic 0 (low) is represented by a voltage of about two volts or less; logic 1 (high) is represented by a higher voltage that is usually about three to five volts.

The inputs and outputs of a microcontroller can be used in isolation to monitor switches, control lamps and relays, etc., or they can be used together as a bus. With suitable coding the signals carried by a bus can represent numbers, letters of the alphabet, or just about anything else.

The microcontroller uses buses to carry data, instructions, etc., internally. Data is carried on the bi-directional data bus, and the memory addresses are handled by the address bus.

The program is stored in ROM, and the ROM contents can not be altered by the program when it is running. The contents of ROM are retained when the unit is switched off.

Microcontrollers have only small amounts of RAM, but RAM is not needed for storing programs. The RAM effectively becomes a set of general purpose data or file registers that can be used as temporary data stores.

The accumulator is the register at the heart of the processor, and it works in conjunction with the ALU (arithmetic logic unit). Virtually all instructions use the ALU and the accumulator.

Program instructions are normally carried out in sequence, working through the ROM from a standard start address. Special instructions enable the program to jump out of the normal sequence.

Some of these jump instructions are conditional, and jump to one address or another depending on the state of a certain bit of a register.

This register is often the status register, which contains flags that are set if certain conditions are met after a mathematical operation.

A clock oscillator controls the rate at which instructions are executed, and PIC processors can operate over a very wide range of clock frequencies.

Microcontrollers are suitable for most applications that are apposite to a logic circuit.

Chapter 2

NUMBERING SYSTEMS AND CODES

When you start learning about logic circuits they can seem to be singularly useless! What distinguishes a logic circuit from an analogue type is that it only deals with two signal levels. As explained in Chapter 1, these are called logic 0 and logic 1, and they are respectively represented by a low voltage (typically about 0 to 2 volts) and a higher voltage that is normally about 3 to 5 volts. While this may appear to give such circuits very limited practical application, in reality they can be applied to almost any need. You only need to look around you in the modern world to see a vast range of applications which now utilise digital circuits. Not only are logic circuits used extensively, but they have totally revolutionised many aspects of modern electronics.

Applied Logic

Some applications are well suited to digital control and it does not take much imagination to see how logic circuits can be put to use in these. As an example, suppose that a circuit must control a row of lights and produce a moving lights display. Each light is either on or off, and this type of control obviously suits the logic way of doing things with just two signal levels. Each light can be switched on by a logic 1 level and switched off by a logic 0 level. It is just a matter of producing a circuit that will produce the right sequence of 0s and 1s at its outputs, and keep repeating this sequence at the required rate.

Most 'real world' applications do not require straightforward on/off switching, but instead deal with quantities of something. For example, a weighing scale does not operate on the basis of something being heavy or not, but deals in actual weights. Digital systems can handle quantities quite easily, and it is just a matter of using a number of digital lines, together with a suitable method of coding. Letters of the alphabet, punctuation marks, etc., are usually represented by ASCII codes, and these use seven lines to carry the codes. Each set of seven 1s and 0s represents a different character. For instance, the code 1010101

27

represents the upper-case letter 'U'.

Numeric values of any magnitude can be represented by a digital circuit, but it requires a large number of digits to represent quite modest values. Even so, with the current technology this still represents by far the easiest way of using electronic circuits to handle numbers. Although the mathematics are being handled in what could be regarded as a rather clumsy fashion, the speed of electronic circuits is such that number-crunching is carried out at very high speeds. Also, the fact that a digital system is operating using 1s and 0s is not normally apparent to the user. There is usually hardware at the input and output of a digital circuit which enables the user to feed in data and extract it using the ordinary decimal numbering system. The user is also protected from raw ASCII codes in much the same way. The user enters letters via a typewriter style keyboard, and the appropriate characters appear on the screen of the monitor or a liquid crystal display. The system gives no hint as to how it is handling the data.

Representing a single quantity using logic signals is clearly quite easy, but how does a digital system handle something like an audio signal that is constantly changing? A digital system can handle varying quantities using a system known as sampling. Although this word is now synonymous with digital audio recording, it is in fact a general term that is applicable to any digital system that deals with what is essentially analogue data. It basically just entails taking a series of readings so that the system tracks the rises and falls in the amplitude of the audio signal, temperature, or whatever.

Strictly speaking, a digital system can not fully accommodate analogue signals since it can never have infinite resolution. With analogue signals that are constantly varying, the input signal is converted into a series of fixed values. No matter how frequently samples are taken, there will always be a jump from one sample value to the next (Fig.2.1). However, provided the resolution of the system is good enough, and samples are taken at a high enough rate, for all practical purposes a digital system will be as good as an analogue equivalent. The jumps from one sample to the next will be of no consequence. In fact, in many areas of electronics it is now true to say that the best digital systems outperform the best

28

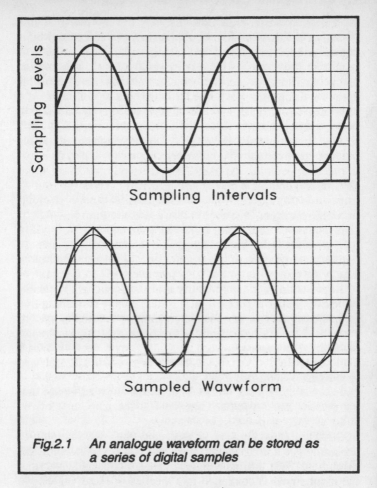

Fig.2.1   An analogue waveform can be stored as
a series of digital samples

analogue types. Whether a digital system is dealing with individual pieces of data, or a series of samples, the resolution is crucial. In other words, is the jump from one level to the next small enough to enable any value to be depicted with good accuracy? The minimum acceptable resolution varies considerably from one application to another.

Although users of digital electronic devices do not normally get involved with all those 1s and 0s, and with ASCII codes, etc., designers of logic circuits can not normally avoid operating at this sort of level. PIC circuit and software design certainly involves a lot of work at this very basic level, and requires a knowledge of the way in which logic systems handle numbers. Therefore, before we consider PIC software and hardware design we will take a fairly detailed look at the basics of numbering systems, and related topics. This type of thing is perhaps not the most stimulating aspect of PIC design, but without a good understanding of the fundamentals it is not possible to undertake PIC hardware or software design.

Bits and Bytes

The numbering system we use in everyday life is, of course, the decimal system, or 'denary' system as it is alternatively known. This method of numbering is based on the number 10, but it is quite possible to have a system based on any number. There is normally no point in doing so, and the old imperial measures which were based on a variety of numbers (12 in the case of feet and inches for example) have now been largely phased out in favour of the metric system.

I suppose that binary could reasonably be regarded as the simplest possible method of numbering. It is based on the number two. In the decimal numbering system the single digit numbers are from 0 to 9, but in binary they are only from 0 to 1. In other words, the only valid numbers for each digit are 0 and 1, and absolutely nothing else is allowed! As already pointed out, representing just two numbers by an electrical signal is very easy. A low voltage it is used to represent a 0, and a higher voltage represents a 1. In the case of ports and other external signals these levels are often called 'low' and 'high' respectively, but these terms are not usually applied to internal signals of a processor. When dealing with internal signals the alternatives of clear (logic 0) and set (logic 1) are often encountered.

Although convenient for the hardware producers, this simple logic system has its limitations and drawbacks. There have been suggestions over the years that circuits which can work directly in decimal will be a practical proposition for widespread use before too long, but there seems to be little real prospect of such a development in the near future. For the time being circuits which work in binary are the only practical ones for general use.

Binary is easier to understand if you first analyse what an ordinary decimal number represents. If we consider the decimal number 238 for instance, the eight represents eight units (10 to the power of 0), the 3 represents three tens (10 to the power of 1), and the 2 represents two hundreds (10 to the power of 2). Things are similar with a binary number such as 1101. Working from right to left again, the columns of numbers respectively represent the units (2 to the power of 0), the 2s (2 to the power of 1), the 4s (2 to the power of 2), the 8s (2 to the power of 3), and so on. 1101 in binary is therefore equivalent to 13 in decimal $(1 + 0 + 4 + 8 = 13)$.

It takes a lot of binary digits to represent numbers of quite modest magnitude, but this is the price that has to be paid for the convenience of simple binary hardware. A binary digit is normally contracted to the term 'bit'. One bit on its own is of limited value, and bits are normally used in groups of eight, or multiples of eight. A group of eight bits is normally termed a 'byte'. A byte can only handle numbers from 0 to 255 (decimal). This is adequate for some purposes, but often larger values must be handled. A 16-bit binary number is usually termed a 'word', and this gives a range of 0 to 65535 (decimal). 32 bits gives a range of 0 to something over four thousand million, which should be adequate for most purposes. A 32-bit number is sometimes termed a 'long word'.

As far as data is concerned, PIC processors deal in 8-bit bytes, and in this respect they are rather crude compared to the microprocessors in the average PC which operate with 32-bit words of data. On the other hand, PIC processors are mainly used in applications where 8-bit operation is adequate. It is possible to use an 8-bit processor to handle 16 or 32-bit words, but the words can only be manipulated 8 bits at a time. This clearly slows things down and complicates matters. PIC processors are not really designed for advanced mathematics on 16 or 32-bit chunks of data, although with suitable software routines they can actually do so. PIC processors use 10, 12, or 14-bit memory addresses, and the convention is that these 10 to 14-bit values are called 'words', even though they fall short of normal 16-bit words. The term 'word' is not well defined, and it can be used to describe any binary value that is more than byte sized.

You can not do much computing without coming across the term 'K'. This is the abbreviation for 'kilobyte', which is a thousand bytes. In fact, to be precise, it is 1024 bytes. This may seem to be an odd number to choose, but a 10-bit binary number covers a range of 0 to 1023, or 1024 different values in other words. The extra 24 on each K is often of no great significance, but it is interesting to note that a computer with a 'megabyte' of memory has 1048576 bytes of memory. Not a million bytes, and some 47K to 48K above the million byte mark. A 'megabyte', which is often abbreviated to just 'M' or 'Mb'', is the usual unit of measurement for large amounts of data, RAM, or whatever.

This table shows the number represented by bits in 16-bit numbers, and this might help to clarify the way in which the binary system operates. The numbers in the table are the ones that the bits represent when a 1 is present in that column of the binary number. If there is a 0 in a column, then that column always contributes 0 to the value of the number. We are using the convention of calling the units column bit 0, running through to bit 15 for the left-most column (not bits 1 to 16). The units column is often called the 'least significant bit', or 'LSB' for short. Bit 31 (or the left-most column that is actually used) is termed the 'most significant bit' or just 'MSB'.

Bit	Decimal Value
0	1
1	2
2	4
3	8
4	16
5	32
6	64
7	128
8	256
9	512
10	1024
11	2048
12	4096
13	8192
14	16384
15	32768

Counting Up

Addition of two binary numbers is a straightforward process which is really more simple than decimal addition. Here is a simple example of binary addition.

First number	240	11110000
Second number	85	01010101
Answer	325	101000101

As with decimal addition, start with the units column and work towards the final column on the left. In this case there is a 1 and a 0 in the units column, giving a 1 in the units column of the answer. In the next column two 0s give a 0 in the answer, and the next two columns are equally straightforward. In the fifth column there are two 1s to be added, giving a total of 2. Of course, in binary the figure 2 does not exist, and this should really be thought of as 10 (one 2 and no units), and it is treated in the same way as 10 in decimal addition. The 0 is placed in the answer, and the 1 is carried forward. In the seventh column this gives a total of 3 in decimal, but in this binary calculation it must be thought of as the binary number 11 (one 2 and one unit). Therefore, 1 is placed in the answer and 1 is carried forward. In the eighth column this gives an answer of 10, and as there are no further columns to be added, both digits are placed in the answer.

Signed Binary

The binary system described so far, which is often called 'direct binary', is inadequate for many practical purposes. It is certainly all that is needed when designing many PIC based projects, but it will not always be sufficient. The main drawback of direct binary is that it can not handle negative numbers. Obviously you can simply add a minus sign ahead of a binary number to indicate that it is a negative number, but you have to bear in mind that for computer applications this is not valid. There is logic 0 and logic 1, but no logic – level!

The normal way around the problem is to use 'signed binary'. With a signed binary number the first bit is used to denote whether the number is positive or negative. The convention is for the first bit to be a 0 for positive numbers and a 1 for negative numbers. With this system the normal 8-bit range of 0 to 255 is replaced with a range of −127 to +127 (11111111 to 01111111). The problem is solved at the expense of decreased maximum magnitude for a given number of bits. Note though, that where two or more bytes (or words or long words) are used together to form a large number, only the most significant bit of the most significant byte needs to be used to indicate the sign of the number. It is not necessary to sacrifice the most significant bit of each byte to this task.

Obviously a certain amount of care needs to be exercised when dealing with binary numbers, and you must know whether you are dealing with direct or signed binary numbers. For instance, 10000001 could be 129 (direct binary) or −1 (signed binary). I have encountered computers which have a binary to decimal conversion facility, and which seem to get confused in this way. Results were as expected for answers up to 32767, but things went completely wrong with higher numbers. This happens where the computer operates with binary numbers of up to 16 bits in length, and it interprets any values it is fed as signed binary. This works fine if you know that it is working with signed binary. It also works fine if it is fed with binary values of 15 bits in length or less. The leading zeros then inform the computer that the number is a positive one, and the right answer is obtained. For numbers of more than 32767 the most significant bit is a 1, telling the computer that it is a negative number, even if you require a direct binary conversion.

In this basic form the signed binary system has its limitations. The problem is that although it can represent a wide range of positive and negative values perfectly adequately, calculations on simple signed binary numbers do not give the correct result. This is of only academic importance to users of high level applications programs and applications software. You give the computer such numeric data, positive, negative, or a mixture of the two, and everything is sorted out for you. It is something that is of greater importance to the low level (assembly language or machine code) programmer. Confusing results can be obtained unless you understand just how the microprocessor is handling things.

Ones Complement

The simple calculation shown below illustrates the problem that occurs using simple signed binary.

First number	16	00010000
Second number	−5	10000101
Answer	−21	10010101

Adding 16 and −5 should obviously give an answer of 11 and not −21. What is happening is that the negative sign of the −5 is being added to the answer so that the answer must always be negative if one of the numbers being added is a negative type. This is clearly incorrect, as in this example. The main bodies of the numbers are simply added together, and their signs are ignored. Negative values therefore increment the figure in the answer rather than decrementing it.

An alternative and related method of handling binary numbers is the 'ones complement' system. Here a negative number is the complement of its positive equivalent. For example, 16 is 00010000 in binary, and so −16 is 11101111 in ones complement binary. In other words, the 0s are simply changed to 1s and the 1s are changed to 0s. This gives much better results when used in calculations, as demonstrated by the example given below.

First number	16	00010000
Second number	−5	11111010
Answer	266	100001010

I suppose that on the face of it this answer is even further from the right answer than when simple signed binary was used. The margin of error is certainly much greater, but the usefulness of this system depends on how the answer is interpreted. The first point to note is that the positive number starts with a 0 while the negative number has a 1 as the first digit. Provided sufficient digits are used this will always be the case, and in this respect

35

the ones complement system is the same as straightforward signed binary. The answer is completely wrong of course, but if the carry is ignored the answer is much closer to the right one. The answer is then 1010 in binary, or ten if converted to decimal. This is just one away from the right answer. So what happens if we try another example and ignore the carry.

First number	32	00100000
Second number	−4	11111011
Answer	27	00011011

As before, the answer is wrong but it is just one less than the right answer (which is of course 28 in this case).

Twos Complement
Clearly this system can be made to operate correctly, and it is just a matter of finding some way of correcting the minor error in the answer. The standard method used with most microprocessors (including the PIC processors) is called 'twos complement'. This differs from ones complement in that once the complement of a number has been produced, one is added to it. Therefore, rather than −5 being represented as 11111010, it becomes 11111011 in twos complement. If we now apply this to one of the examples given earlier we obtain the following result.

First number	16	00010000
Second number	−5	11111011
Answer	11	00001011

This time, provided we ignore the carry, we do indeed obtain the correct answer of 11. This is a convenient way of handling subtraction (for microprocessors if not for humans), since subtraction can be carried out by the same circuit that handles addition. To handle a calculation such as 45 − 25 the value of 25 is converted to twos complement and then added to 45. In other words, instead of handling this calculation in the form 45 − 25 it is undertaken in the form 45 + (−25), and either way the answer is 20.

The table given below shows some sample numbers in twos complement form, and this should help to clarify the system for you. Note that, like ordinary signed binary, the first digit is used to indicate whether the number is positive or negative.

Number	Positive	Negative
0	00000000	00000000
1	00000001	11111111
2	00000010	11111110
3	00000011	11111101
4	00000100	11111100
32	00100000	11100000
126	01111110	10000010
127	01111111	10000001
128	01000000	10000000

Note that with 8-bit twos complement numbers the range is from −127 to +128 (not −127 to +127 as with simple signed binary).

So far we have only considered calculations where the answer is a positive quantity, but the twos complement system works equally well if the answer is negative. This point is demonstrated by the example provided below.

First number	16	00010000
Second number	−31	11100001
Answer	−15	11110001

The two complement system also functions properly when the two numbers being added are both negative, as in this example:

First number	−4	11111100
Second number	−8	11111000
Answer	−12	11110100

Binary Coded Decimal

Several microprocessors can operate using another form of binary called 'binary coded decimal', or just 'BCD'. This is a somewhat less compact and efficient form of binary, it is generally somewhat slower, and it is not used in most applications. It does have its advantages though, and the main one is that it can be used to provide a very high degree of precision. The PIC processors do not have any instructions which use BCD, but you may wish to drive displays or other devices using BCD.

BCD uses four binary bits (often termed a 'nibble') to represent each decimal digit. The system operates in the manner shown below.

Decimal Number	Binary Code
0	0000
1	0001
2	0010
3	0011
4	0100
5	0101
6	0110
7	0111
8	1000
9	1001

The binary number is in fact just the ordinary binary bit code for the number concerned, and it is only for numbers of more than 9 that the system is different. The binary codes from 1010 to 1111 are unused, and all two digit decimal numbers require 8-bit BCD codes. For instance, the decimal number 64 would be represented by the 8-bit BCD code 01100100. The first four bits (0110) represent the six, and the second four bits (0100) represent the four. Each byte can therefore represent any two digit decimal number from 0 to 99, which compares to a range of 0 to 255 for an ordinary 8-bit binary number. This helps to contribute to the relative inefficiency of the BCD system. Of course, when a nibble is incremented by 1 from a value of 1001 (9 in decimal) it does not go to 1010 (which is an illegal code in BCD), but cycles back to 0000. A carry forward of 1 should then be taken to the next BCD nibble. Since the PIC processors do not operate directly in BCD, you must provide the conversion from direct binary to BCD using suitable software routines. Look-up tables are the normal method for handling this type of thing.

With BCD there is no difficulty in handling large numbers, and it is just a matter of using several bytes in order to accommodate the required number of digits. Negative numbers and decimal points can also be handled with ease by this system, but this requires several additional bits. This information is usually carried in the most significant bits (i.e. the left hand end of the number), but you can design the software and hardware to handle this type of thing in any way that you see fit.

Hexadecimal

Hexadecimal is a numbering system that you are almost certain to use a great deal when undertaking PIC programming. In fact it will be the main numbering system that you use. The hexadecimal name is usually abbreviated to just 'hex'. A problem with binary numbers is that they tend to have many digits with each one being a 0 or a 1, which makes them rather difficult to deal with in many circumstances. For instance, dealing with 10 or 12 bit addresses in their binary form would probably be beyond most people's ability, as would dealing with eight-bit data values. On the other hand, binary numbers give a graphic representation of each bit in the register of a microprocessor, control register of a peripheral chip, output terminals of a PIC port, or whatever. This is something that is often important, but is especially so when dealing with a microcontroller and its ports. Decimal numbers are much easier to deal with in that they are much shorter and are in a more familiar form. Unfortunately, a decimal number does not give much idea of the state of each bit in its binary equivalent. Converting a decimal number to its binary equivalent is not a particularly quick or easy process (without the aid of some computerised help anyway). Decimal numbers are consequently rather inconvenient when things must be visualised on a bit by bit basis.

The hexadecimal system gives the best of both worlds in that it takes just a few digits to represent even quite large numbers, and it is in fact slightly better than the decimal numbering system in this respect. On the other hand, it is quite easy to convert hexadecimal numbers to their binary equivalents when the state of each bit must be known. The conversion process is quite simple even with very large numbers. The hexadecimal system is based on the number 16, and there are sixteen single digit numbers. Obviously the numbers we normally use in the decimal system are inadequate for hexadecimal as there are six too few of them. This problem is overcome by augmenting them with the first six digits of the alphabet (A to F). It is from this that the system derives its name. The table given on page 41 helps to explain the way in which the hexadecimal system operates.

What makes hexadecimal so convenient is the ease with which multi-digit numbers can be converted into binary equivalents. The reason for this is that each hexadecimal digit represents four binary bits. Take the hexadecimal number A3 in the table for example – digit A represents 1010 in binary, and the digit 3 converts to 0011. A3 therefore represents 10100011 in binary. You may find that you can memorise each of the sixteen 4-bit binary codes represented by hexadecimal digits, but a little mental arithmetic is all that is needed in order to make the conversion if you can not.

The digits in a hexadecimal number represent, working from right to left, the number of units, 16s, 256s, 4096s, 65536s, 1048576s, and 268435450s (approx.). In general computing you are unlikely to use hexadecimal numbers of more than eight digits in length, and mostly you will probably only deal with hexadecimal numbers having four digits or less. When dealing with PIC processors you should not need to use hexadecimal numbers having more than three digits, and in most cases you will use only one or two digit numbers.

Decimal	Hexadecimal	Binary
0	0	0000
1	1	0001
2	2	0010
3	3	0011

4	4	0100
5	5	0101
6	6	0110
7	7	0111
8	8	1000
9	9	1001
10	A	1010
11	B	1011
12	C	1100
13	D	1101
14	E	1110
15	F	1111
16	10	10000
17	11	10001
18	12	10010
163	A3	10100011

Octal

Although the octal numbering system was much used in computer circles at one time, it seems to have fallen from favour. Hexadecimal now seems to have superseded it. As its name suggests, it is based on the number 8. The columns of figures therefore represent the units, 8s, 64s, 512s, 4096s, 32768s, etc. Only the first eight digits (0 to 7) of the decimal numbering system are utilised by the octal system, and so neither 8 nor 9 are legal characters in octal.

In common with hexadecimal, octal keeps the number of digits in large numbers down to reasonable proportions, but it can easily be converted into binary if the state of each bit must be known. Whereas each hexadecimal digit represents a four bit binary code, each octal digit represents just three binary bits. With modern computing being based on 8-bit bytes, or multiples of eight bits, the 3-bit octal codes are less than totally convenient. It is probably this factor that has led to its decline in favour of the hexadecimal system. Here is a list of octal digits and the three bit binary codes that they represent:

Octal Digit	Binary Code
0	000
1	001
2	010
3	011
4	100
5	101
6	110
7	111
8	001000

As with hexadecimal digits, the binary codes they represent are just the standard codes for the numbers concerned. It is probably not worthwhile taking the time to familiarise yourself with the octal numbering system as it is rarely, if ever, encountered in practice these days, and you are unlikely to use it in conjunction with PIC processors.

Conversions

Conversion from hexadecimal to binary is, as we have already seen, fairly straightforward. With a little experience a little mental arithmetic is all that is needed to make this type of conversion. Conversion in the opposite direction is equally simple. It is just a matter of breaking down the binary number into four-bit groups and then converting each group to its corresponding hexadecimal digit.

Conversions that involve decimal numbers are a little more difficult to deal with. The easy way of handling the problem is to use a computer to make the conversion (or possibly a scientific calculator). Most BASICs can provide a hexadecimal to decimal conversion. If the computer accepts hexadecimal numbers with (say) an '&H' prefix to indicate that they are in hexadecimal, then giving the instruction:

PRINT &HXXXX RETURN

where 'XXXX' is the hexadecimal number to be converted, should result in the decimal equivalent being printed on the screen. A conversion in the opposite direct might also be possible, and this is most commonly found in the form of a HEX$ function. You may even find that decimal to octal conversion is possible using an OCT$ function (as in Amiga BASIC for instance), although these days such a function would seem to be of largely academic interest.

Bitwise Operations

In computing, numbers are not only manipulated using the normal mathematical functions. There are also the 'bitwise' operations called 'AND', 'OR', and 'XOR'. These compare two binary numbers (literally) bit-by-bit, and the answer produced depends on the combination of 0s and 1s present in each column. ANDing produces a 1 in the answer only if there is a 1 in that column of both the numbers being ANDed. In other words, if a bit is set to 1 in the first number and the second, a 1 is placed in that bit of the answer. Hence the 'AND' name of this logic operation. Here is a simple ANDing example:

First number	15	00001111
Second number	243	11110011
Answer	3	00000011

The answers obtained from bitwise operations can tend to look a bit random unless you consider what is happening on a bit by bit basis. A common use of the bitwise AND function is when less than all eight bits of a byte must be read. For instance, assume that we wish to know the state of bit 3 of a register or input port. Most computer systems do not provide any means of reading just one bit of a port or register, although the PIC processors do actually include some bit oriented instructions. Anyway, one way around the problem is to use a bitwise AND operation to mask off the unwanted bits. In this case bit 3 represents eight when it is set to logic 1, and so the masking number to use is eight (00000100 in binary). In the answer all the bits except bit 3 must be set to zero, as there is no way they can be set to 1 in both numbers. The situation is different for bit 3, where both bits could be at logic 1 if the

43

second number also has this bit set to 1. The answer therefore reflects the state of bit 3 in the second number, and is eight if this bit is at logic 1, or zero if it is at logic 0. The ANDing provides the desired function with, in effect, only the required bit being read.

It is possible to read more than one bit if desired, and in a PIC processor context this is the way that bitwise ANDing would normally be used. Just set any bits which must be read to logic 1 in the masking number – set any bits which must be masked off to logic 0 in the masking number. As a couple of examples, to read the least significant nibble a masking number of 15 (00001111 in binary) would be used, and to read the most significant nibble the masking number would be 240 (11110000 in binary).

Bitwise ORing is a similar process to ANDing, but a 1 is placed in a bit of the answer if there is a 1 in that bit of the first number, or the second number, or both. XORing (exclusive ORing) differs from normal (inclusive) ORing in that it will place a 1 in a bit of the answer if there is a 1 in that bit of the first number or the second, but not if there is a 1 in both bits of these numbers. This could reasonably be regarded as the true OR function, but it has been designated the XOR function. The following example shows how these two types of bitwise operation can produce different answers.

First Number	15	00001111
Second Number	85	01010101
ORed Result	95	01011111
First Number	15	00001111
Second Number	85	01010101
XORed Result	90	01011010

The main use of the bitwise OR function is to permit some bits of a register to be altered without changing the states of the

44

other bits. Suppose that you wish to set bits 0 to 3 of a register to 1. You could simply write a value of 15 (00001111) to the register, but if any of bits 4 to 7 were originally set to 1, this would result in them being changed to zero. The PIC processors have bit oriented instructions, and using one of these it would be possible to set each bit to 1, but it would require a separate instruction for each bit. This might still be your preferred way of doing things. The alternative is to read the register, and bitwise OR the result with a suitable value. Determining this value is quite straightforward. A one is used in the bits that must be set to one, and a zero is used in the other bits. In our example it is bits 0 to 3 that must be set to one, and bits 3 to 7 that must be left unchanged. This gives a masking number of 15. If you look at the bitwise OR example shown previously, where a value of 85 (01010101 in binary) is ORed with 15, you will note that the lower four bits in the answer are all set to one, but the upper four bits remain unchanged. This gives the desired result using just a single instruction.

If you needed to set the lower nibble to zero rather one, it is a bitwise AND operation that would be used. Use a one in any bits that must be left unaltered, and a zero in bits that must be zero. A value of 240 (11110000) would therefore be used to set the four least significant bits to zero, as shown in this example.

Number In Register	85	01010101
Masking Number	240	11110000
Answer	80	01010000

The bitwise XOR function perhaps has fewer practical uses than the AND and OR functions, but it can occasionally prove to be useful. It is possible to complement the bits in a byte (change the 1s to 0s and vice versa) by XORing the byte with 255 (11111111 in binary). However, the PIC processors have a complement instruction that provides this function.

Rotate and Shift
Microprocessors normally have shift and (or) rotate instructions, and the PIC microcontrollers have rotate left and

45

rotate right instructions. In a basic rotate left instruction the bits in the byte are all moved one place to the left, and the leftmost bit (bit 7) is moved into the space left vacant by bit 0. A right rotation is the opposite of this, with all the bits being moved one place to the right, and bit 0 being moved into the space left vacant by shifted bit 7. Figure 2.2 shows 'before and after' examples for both types of rotation. Shift instructions, incidentally, are the same except that any bits which are moved out of the register are simply discarded, rather than being moved round to the other end of the register.

The PIC processors provide slightly more complex rotate instructions that involve an extra bit called the carry flag. The rotations are through the carry flag, which simply means that the digit which is displaced from one end of the byte is placed into the carry flag rather than being moved to the other end of the byte. This is not the sole function of the carry flag, and it is used whenever there is a spare bit. For example, if 255 and 2 are added together, in binary it gives this result:

255	11111111
2	00000010
Total (257)	100000001

This calculation gives a nine-bit answer, which is clearly one bit too many for an eight bit register. The one in the most significant bit is therefore stored in the carry bit, or carry flag as it is generally called. The eight bit data registers of a PIC processor can not accommodate the carry, but conditional instructions can provide one function or an alternative depending on the state of the carry flag. With suitable software the 'lost' bit can be rescued.

Returning to the rotation instructions, you really have to consider the carry flag to be part of the register which is being 'rotated'. If the carry bit is set to one when the rotation instruction is carried out, this one will be placed in the bit of the register that has just been emptied. Further rotation instructions in the same direction result in the bit in the carry flag being stored in one end of the data register, while the bit

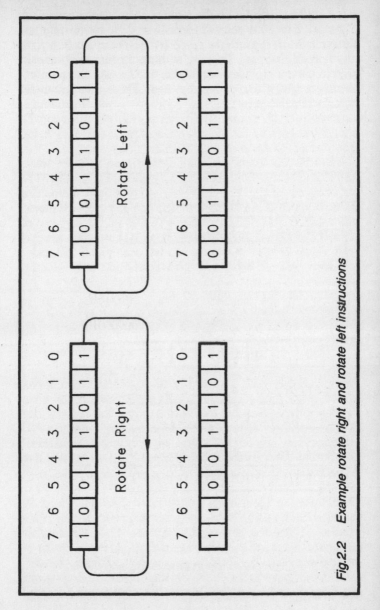

Fig.2.2 Example rotate right and rotate left instructions

ousted at the other end of the register goes into the carry flag. Figures 2.3 and 2.4 show the result of three rotate right and three rotate left instructions respectively. These should help to clarify both processes. Looking at things in numerical terms, a shift to the left provides a multiplication by two, and a shift to the right gives a division by two. These two examples demonstrate this point.

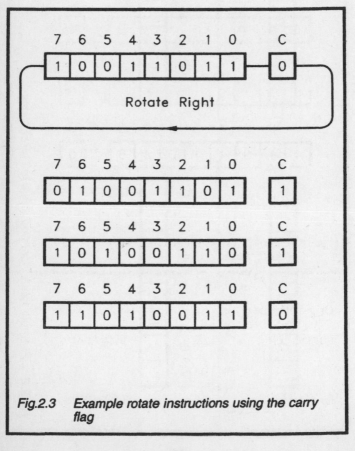

Fig.2.3   Example rotate instructions using the carry flag

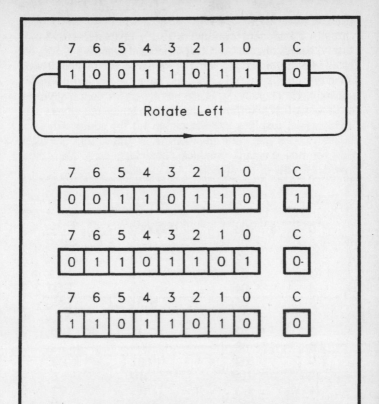

Fig.2.4 This example shows the result of three rotate left instructions

Original Value	14	00001110
Shifted Left	28	00011100
Original Value	14	00001110
Shifted Right	7	00000111

ASCII Codes

Virtually all modern computers use a character set that is closely based on the ASCII (American Standard Code for Information Interchange) set. They are also used when driving liquid crystal displays (LCDs) that have the ability to display alphanumeric characters. These are seven bit codes, giving a maximum of 128 different characters. Many computers and liquid crystal displays use the eighth bit for additional, non-standard codes (i.e. code numbers from 128 to 255 are often used for non-standard graphics characters, etc.). This table provides details of the standard ASCII codes.

Decimal	Hex	Binary	Character
0	00	0000000	NULL
1	01	0001	SOH
2	02	0010	STX
3	03	0011	ETX
4	04	0100	EOT
5	05	0101	ENQ
6	06	0110	ACK
7	07	0111	BEL
8	08	1000	BS
9	09	1001	HT
10	0A	1010	LF
11	0B	1011	VT
12	0C	1100	FF
13	0D	1101	CR
14	0E	1110	SO
15	0F	1111	SI
16	10	0010000	DLE
17	11	0001	DC1
18	12	0010	DC2
19	13	0011	DC3
20	14	0100	DC4
21	15	0101	NAK
22	16	0110	SYN
23	17	0111	ETB
24	18	1000	CAN
25	19	1001	EM

Decimal	Hex	Binary	Character
26	1A	1010	SUB
27	1B	1011	ESC
28	1C	1100	FS
29	1D	1101	GS
30	1E	1110	RS
31	1F	1111	US
32	20	0100000	[SPACE]
33	21	0001	!
34	22	0010	"
35	23	0011	[HASH]
36	24	0100	$
37	25	0101	%
38	26	0110	&
39	27	0111	'
40	28	1000	(
41	29	1001	)
42	2A	1010	*
43	2B	1011	+
44	2C	1100	,
45	2D	1101	-
46	2E	1110	.
47	2F	1111	/
48	30	0110000	0
49	31	0001	1
50	32	0010	2
51	33	0011	3
52	34	0100	4
53	35	0101	5
54	36	0110	6
55	37	0111	7
56	38	1000	8
57	39	1001	9
58	3A	1010	:
59	3B	1011	;
60	3C	1100	<
61	3D	1101	=
62	3E	1110	>
63	3F	1111	?

Decimal	Hex	Binary	Character
64	40	1000000	@
65	41	0001	A
66	42	0010	B
67	43	0011	C
68	44	0100	D
69	45	0101	E
70	46	0110	F
71	47	0111	G
72	48	1000	H
73	49	1001	I
74	4A	1010	J
75	4B	1011	K
76	4C	1100	L
77	4D	1101	M
78	4E	1110	N
79	4F	1111	O
80	50	1010000	P
81	51	0001	Q
82	52	0010	R
83	53	0011	S
84	54	0100	T
85	55	0101	U
86	56	0110	V
87	57	0111	W
88	58	1000	X
89	59	1001	Y
90	5A	1010	Z
91	5B	1011	[
92	5C	1100	\
93	5D	1101	]
94	5E	1110	^
95	5F	1111	_
96	60	1100000	`
97	61	0001	a
98	62	0010	b
99	63	0011	c
100	64	0100	d
101	65	0101	e

Decimal	Hex	Binary	Character
102	66	0110	f
103	67	0111	g
104	68	1000	h
105	69	1001	i
106	6A	1010	j
107	6B	1011	k
108	6C	1100	l
109	6D	1101	m
110	6E	1110	n
111	6F	1111	o
112	70	1110000	p
113	71	0001	q
114	72	0010	r
115	73	0011	s
116	74	0100	t
117	75	0101	u
118	76	0110	v
119	77	0111	w
120	78	1000	x
121	79	1001	y
122	7A	1010	z
123	7B	1011	{
124	7C	1100	l
125	7D	1101	}
126	7E	1110	~
127	7F	1111	DEL

Finally

For some initial and fairly basic PIC programming you can get by with an understanding of direct binary and the hexadecimal numbering system, so you should at the very least make sure that you are reasonably familiar with both of these topics. Without a working knowledge of direct binary and hexadecimal it is not possible to set up the input and output ports, read the ports, etc. You can 'brush up' on bitwise operations, rotation instructions, etc., as and when you need them. The ASCII codes are not something you need to learn, and the ASCII table provided previously should be useful for reference purposes if you produce a system that writes information to an alphanumeric liquid crystal display.

Chapter 3

SPECIFICS

So far we have only considered the subject of microcontrollers in fairly broad terms. In this chapter we will take a more detailed look at things, and in particular we will look at the internal workings of the PIC series of microcontrollers. The basic function of any microprocessor is to move data around and to process it, and the microprocessor at the heart of a PIC processor is certainly no exception to this. Although there are similarities in the internal arrangements of various microprocessors, and also similarities in the instructions that they perform, there are also large differences from one microprocessor to another. If you are familiar with microprocessors such as the Z80 and 68000 series you should not find it too difficult to adjust to using PIC processors. On the other hand, it is only fair to point out that the PIC series of chips are very simple in comparison with most other microprocessors and you will need to adjust to their more simple way of doing things. Also, there are one or two fundamental differences between PIC processors and devices such as the Z80 and 68000, and these also necessitate a certain amount of adjustment.

ROM Types
As pointed out in Chapter 1, the program for a PIC chip is stored in its ROM (read only memory). There is more than one type of ROM, and most of the PIC chips are equipped with what is called EPROM (erasable programmable read only memory). Your program is placed in the EPROM using a system that is normally in the form of a PC equipped with appropriate software and some fairly simple hardware. This is not a process we will consider here, but it is not difficult to program PIC chips using the systems that are now readily available. Because the contents of EPROM are erasable, once a chip has been programmed it is possible to re-use it by erasing the contents of the EPROM and re-programming the chip. The EPROM is erased by subjecting it to short wavelength ultra-

violet 'light' for about 20 minutes, and suitable erasure units are readily available. An EPROM eraser is basically just a light-tight box having a pad of conductive foam for the chips at the bottom, and the ultra-violet tube at the top.

Some of the PIC processors are available without the necessary window to enable the ultra-violet 'light' to reach the silicon chip, and their EPROM is therefore not erasable. Consequently, once one of these chips has been programmed it can not be re-programmed and re-used in a different application. Perhaps of more importance, these non-erasable chips are not suitable for developing PIC based systems. The general idea is to use an erasable chip when developing new systems, with the chip being erased and re-programmed as many times as is necessary to perfect the software. The finished product is then built using a non-erasable PIC chip. These are very much cheaper than the erasable versions. As well as a programmer and an erasure unit you therefore need at least one or two erasable PIC chips in order to develop PIC based systems. All the PIC processors are avai lable in true EPROM and non-erasable versions.

The non-erasable chips are sometimes called OTP (one-time programmable) chips incidentally. Do not be tempted to use one-time programmable chips for development purposes as this will almost certainly be a false economy. You are likely to gain little from the experience but a bin full of wasted PIC processors! The erasable PIC chips have a life of over 10,000 programming and erasure cycles, which in theory means that they should never wear out. In reality they should last for a great many years unless you are careless and 'zap' one from time to time. Physical wear on the pins is probably the limiting factor rather than the number of erasure and programming cycles they can withstand.

A few PIC processors are equipped with EEROM (electronically erasable read only memory). These chips differ from the true EPROM type in that they can be erased electronically, and can not be 'wiped' using an ultra-violet light box. The EEROM chips are more convenient to use because they can be erased more quickly, but as yet there is a limited choice of EEROM chips, and you obviously need a compatible programmer/eraser system before you can use them.

Take Your PIC

There are currently several versions of the PIC processor that are generally available, and although these are basically the same 'at heart', there are still important differences from one PIC chip to another. The main differences are in the number and type of ports that they offer, and in the amount of RAM and ROM that they contain. Here we will restrict ourselves to the mainstream PIC devices, since these provide the best starting point. I would recommend that you become familiar with these before trying the more exotic types, or the ultra-simple eight-pin devices that have recently been introduced.

The most basic of the mainstream PIC chips are contained in ordinary 18-pin d.i.l. plastic encapsulations, and have two input/output ports. These consist of one 4-bit port and one 8-bit port (i.e. a total of 12 input/output lines), and they are respectively designated port A and port B. Just 12 input/output lines is obviously something of a limitation, but it is perfectly adequate for many practical applications. The versatility of the ports is increased by having each line individually

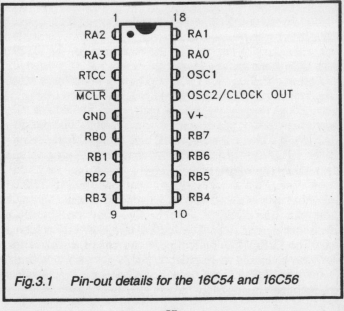

Fig.3.1   Pin-out details for the 16C54 and 16C56

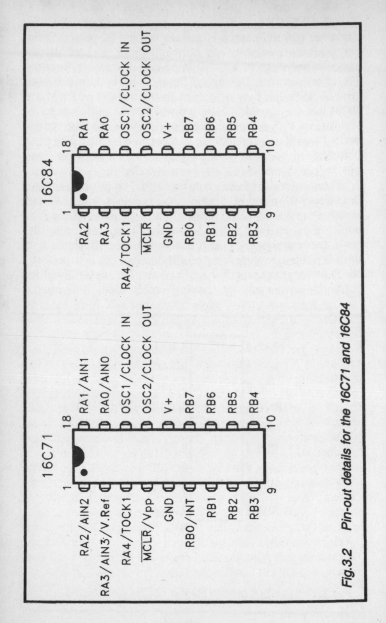

Fig.3.2   Pin-out details for the 16C71 and 16C84

58

programmable to operate as an input or an output. If you need (say) 10 input lines and two outputs, the two ports of a simple PIC processor are able to oblige. The 16C54 and 16C56 are two basic PIC processors which have two ports, and the pin-out diagram for these is provided in Figure 3.1. The only difference between these two chips is that the 16C54 has 512 bytes of ROM whereas the 16C56 has 1024 bytes (1K).

Next up the scale in terms of complexity are the 16C71 and 16C84 which respectively have 1024 bytes of EPROM and EEROM. In addition to the differences in their ROMs, the 16C71 has a four channel analogue to digital converter in place of its four bit input port (port A). Port A can still be used as a digital type if preferred, or it can even be configured to operate in mixed digital/analogue modes. The analogue capability is clearly a very useful facility that can be utilised in numerous control and measurement applicables. Pin-out details for both these chips are provided in Figure 3.2.

The 16C55 and 16C57 can be used in applications that require larger numbers of digital input and output lines. These two devices respectively have 512 bytes and 2048 bytes of EPROM, and are housed in a 28-pin DIL encapsulation. They have the same pin-out configuration (Fig.3.3). You will notice from this that they have three ports, which are two 8-bit ports and one 4-bit type. This gives some 20 input/output lines, which is more than enough for the vast majority of applications. However, the 17C42 has even more input/output ports giving no less than 33 input/output lines. Probably few practical applications require anything like this number of inputs and outputs, but this chip is there if you should have an application that does.

Having so many versions of the PIC microcontroller can be a bit confusing at first, but Table 1 should help to clarify matters. This provides some basic information about the amount of ROM and RAM, the input/output ports, etc., for a range of PIC processors. This information should make it easier to select a suitable chip for a given application. Some of the information given in this table might not make much sense at present, but all will be revealed later.

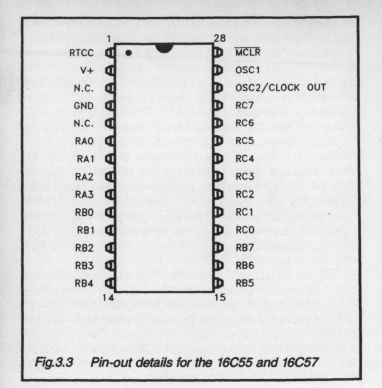

Fig.3.3 Pin-out details for the 16C55 and 16C57

Table 1

	16C54	16C55	16C56	16C57	16C71	16C84
EPROM	512	512	1K	2K	1K	1K
RAM	32	32	32	80	36	36
Digital I/O	4 + 8	4 + 8 + 8	4 + 8	4 + 8 + 8	5 + 8	5 + 8
Analogue Inputs	0	0	0	0	4	0
Instructions	33	33	33	33	35	35
Instruction Bits	12	12	12	12	14	14
Stack Size	2	2	2	2	8	8
Pins	18	28	18	28	18	18
Interrupts	No	No	No	No	Yes	Yes
PU Timer	No	No	No	No	Yes	Yes

Programming

While I do not intend to give a detailed account of programming and erasing PIC chips, it would probably be as well to take a quick look at what is required in order to undertake PIC project development. It is definitely advisable to start with one of the PIC development systems that are now readily available. These provide you with everything you will need to program PIC processors, with the obvious exception of the PC. In theory it is not essential to have a PC in order to undertake PIC programming, but in practice you will find the going very tough unless you have access to a PC. Fortunately, many of the PIC development systems are supplied with software that will run on practically any PC. Therefore, you do not need the last word in PC technology in order to program chips. A PIC development system normally consists of three main components. These are:

1. An assembler program which runs on the PC, and assembles your program into machine code that can be run by the PIC processor. The processor deals with binary values, and it is not just the data it handles that is in binary. The instructions are also in this form, but it is obviously awkward and inconvenient for the programmer to work directly in binary. The standard way around this is for the programmer to write the programs in assembly language, which uses a mnemonic for each program instruction. A mnemonic is simply a short name which is much easier to remember than the binary code number, and is quicker to use than the full name of the instruction. As an example, the no operation instruction has the mnemonic 'NOP'. The assembler takes the assembly language source code and converts it into corresponding binary object code that the PIC processor can run. In fact all practical assemblers provide more help than simply converting mnemonics into the corresponding binary numbers, but they do not provide anything like as much help as a high level language such as BASIC or Pascal. Although the PIC processors all use the same basic instruction set, unfortunately they do not all use the same object code. Consequently, you must ensure that you obtain an assembler that can handle the object code for the particular PIC processor or processors that you will be using.

2. The programmer that is used to 'blow' your programs into the PIC chips. In most cases this is something pretty basic, and it usually seems to be nothing more than a small printed circuit board that connects to one of the computer's ports via a ribbon cable. Serial and parallel port programmers are available, and it probably makes little difference which type you use. In theory a parallel port can handle data transfers at a higher rate than a serial port, but this is unlikely to be of any significance in the present context. The PIC chips come in a variety of shapes and sizes, and you obviously need to make sure that the programmer can handle the particular chips you intend to use. The system will include matching software that takes the data from the assembler and loads it into the PIC chips via the programmer hardware.

3. Finally, most systems include a PIC simulator which enables you to test your programs without actually 'blowing' them into a PIC chip and trying them for real. Testing a PIC chip in an actual circuit and erasing its EPROM if it does not work properly is a time consuming process and a good simulator can save a great deal of time. PIC chips normally operate at very high speeds, but the simulator runs the program at a greatly reduced rate so that you can see exactly what is happening. Alternatively, the simulator may run at high speed but you will be able to select points in the program where the simulation stops so that you can examine the contents of the chip's registers. The up-marked alternative to a simulator is an emulator. A simulation is normally achieved solely in software, but an emulator includes hardware, and it tries to accurately mimic the selected PIC chip.

In addition to some PICs and the development system you will need an EPROM eraser. This is basically just a small metal box which contains an ultra-violet tube and some conductive foam into which the PIC chips are placed. The conductive foam ensures that the chips are safe while they are in the eraser, and that they will not be 'zapped' by static electricity. Unfortunately, EPROM erasers are quite expensive, and one reason for this is that the special ultra-violet tubes are not exactly cheap. Ordinary ultra-violet tubes of the type used in 'sun-ray' lamps are not suitable for this application as they do not provide the short wavelength ultra-violet radiation needed to erase EPROMs. The same is true of ultra-violet light-boxes that are intended for exposing photosensitive copper laminate boards. Note that short wavelength ultra-violet 'light' is dangerous, and can easily damage your eyesight. Always use a proper eraser, and use it in strict accordance with the manufacturer's instructions. When developing PIC projects you only need to erase one or two chips at a time, and a very basic eraser should therefore be perfectly adequate.

Reset

At switch-on a microprocessor system always goes through a reset routine which ensures that all the registers are in the correct states before the first program instruction is performed. There are two methods of resetting PIC processors, and one of these relies on an external C-R circuit to provide a negative pulse to the 'master clear' input of the processor. Figure 3.4 shows the recommended C-R reset circuit. R2 is needed to ensure that an excessive current can not flow into the 'master clear' input of the processor, and its value should be between 100 ohms and 1 kilohm. D1 simply ensures that C1 rapidly discharges when the circuit is switched off, so that the reset circuit operates normally next time the unit is switched on. The values of R1 and C1 are selected to give the required reset pulse duration, but note that the value of R1 must be less than 40 kilohms. If a higher value is used there is a danger that the voltage drop across R1 will be so high that the circuit will be held in the reset state.

In most cases an external reset circuit of this type is not required. It is only needed where the power supply has a low rise-time, or where a low frequency crystal controlled clock oscillator is used. A long reset pulse of around 100 milliseconds or more is then needed to ensure that everything has settled down properly by the time the processor performs the first instruction of the program.

The alternative is to use the internal reset circuit, and in order to do this it is merely necessary to connect the 'master clear' input to the +5 volt supply rail. The PIC processors have a built in starter-up timer which ensures that the clock oscillator

63

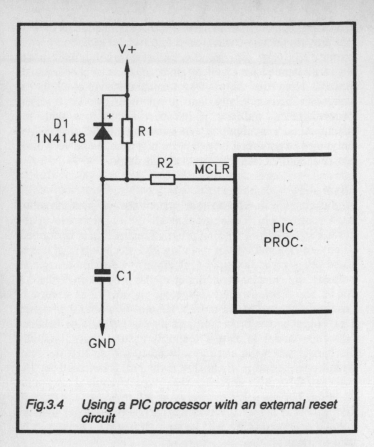

Fig.3.4   Using a PIC processor with an external reset circuit

has time to settle down and operate normally before it starts clocking the processor. The internal reset circuit makes use of this timer to provide a switch-on delay for the entire chip, and to provide the necessary reset signals to the various stages of the chip that require them. This reset circuit is suitable for most situations, but the power supply must reach its full potential within 18 milliseconds of switch-on. This means that the supply only has to rise by about 50 millivolts per millisecond, and most supplies will easily exceed this rate. An external reset circuit is normally only required when a low frequency crystal controlled clock oscillator is used.

Clocking On

The PIC processors can be used with two basic types of clock circuit, but there are four PIC clock oscillator modes. With some PIC processors you have to make sure you obtain a suitable version of the processor for the type of clock circuit you wish to use. Where high precision is needed a crystal controlled clock oscillator should be utilised. The circuit for a crystal clock oscillator appears in Figure 3.5 The active circuitry is an integral part of the PIC processor, and the only discrete components required are the crystal itself plus one resistor, and two capacitors. The resistor will not always be required, and it is only needed where the oscillator is otherwise slightly too lively. This overdriving of the oscillator can result

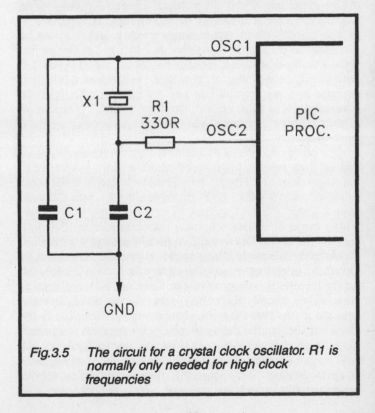

Fig.3.5   The circuit for a crystal clock oscillator. R1 is normally only needed for high clock frequencies

in an incorrect output frequency, with the oscillator usually operating at about half its intended output frequency.

Three of the PIC modes are crystal controlled types, and the normal crystal clock mode is called the 'XT' mode. This mode operates with crystals from 100 kilohertz to four megahertz. The PIC clock oscillator circuit is intended for use with parallel resonant crystals and not the series resonant type. Ceramic resonators should also give satisfactory results, but the frequency stability of resonators is inferior to that of crystals. C1 and C2 are normally equal in value, and this value must be chosen to suit the clock frequency used. A capacitance of about 22 to 33 picofarads is about right for clock frequencies in the range 1 megahertz to 4 megahertz. Lower frequencies require a higher capacitance, and the value of about 68 picofarads is suitable for a clock frequency of 500 kilohertz. Crystals seem to vary slightly from one make to another, and it might be necessary to do a little 'tweaking' in order to get things just right. On the other hand, reliable results are usually provided with a fairly broad range of capacitance values, and it is only if you use a 'fussy' crystal that any 'tweaking' is likely to be necessary. Note that ceramic resonators usually require a slightly higher capacitance value than a crystal operating at the same frequency.

The other two crystal oscillator modes are HS (high speed) and LP (low power). High speed means a clock frequency in the range eight to 20 megahertz. The clock circuit is the same as the one for standard (XT) operation, but C1 and C2 must have a lower value of around 15 to 22 picofarads. The low power mode also uses the same oscillator circuit, but with higher values for C1 and C2 (typically around 100 to 220 picofarads). This mode is used with low frequency crystals, and these have operating frequencies of around 30 to 200 kilohertz. As the three types of crystal controlled chips all use the same basic clock circuit, there may seem to be no differences between them. There may be some internal differences in the clock circuits, but the main differences are the maximum clock frequencies. LP devices only function up to 200kHz, XT devices will function at up to 4MHz, and HS chips will operate at up to 20MHz. With some PIC devices (including the re-programmable types) the required type of clock circuit is selected when programming the device, and operation at up to 20MHz is supported. With most other members of the PIC family there is a different chip for each of the four clock types.

It is possible to use an external clock oscillator with any PIC processor that is intended for use with a crystal clock circuit (i.e. chips that are designed for XT, HS, or LP clocks). The clock signal must be at logic levels that are compatible with PIC processors, and the clock frequency must obviously be within the normal operating range of the type of processor you are using. The clock signal is applied to the CLKIN terminal of the processor. In most cases there is no point in using an external clock circuit, but I suppose it could be useful to do so if you want to use a series resonant crystal in the clock circuit. Do not try to use an external clock circuit with a processor that is not designed for use with a crystal clock oscillator.

The fourth type of clock oscillator is a simple C-R type which uses the circuit of Figure 3.6. This is really just a simple relaxation oscillator, which repeatedly charges and discharges C1 via R1. This type of oscillator is delightfully simple, and avoids the cost of a crystal or ceramic resonator. However, it does have one or two major drawbacks, and one of these is that it is only suitable for use at frequencies of up to four megahertz. In practice this is sufficient for most applications, but there is a further problem which is simply the lack of good frequency stability and predictability. The output frequency changes significantly with variations in the supply voltage, and simple oscillator circuits of this type usually have poor temperature stability.

The lack of temperature stability is largely caused by the temperature characteristic of the timing capacitor. Using a high quality component here minimises the problem, but a simple C-R oscillator never achieves anything approaching the frequency stability of a crystal oscillator. The lack of predictability is due in part to the tolerances of the resistor and capacitor which are far larger than those for a crystal or ceramic resonator. It is also due to stray capacitance in the clock circuit of the PIC processor itself, plus other factors governed by the internal circuit. Although the stray capacitance is quite small, it can be comparable to the value of C1 when the circuit is used at high output frequencies. In fact C1 can be omitted if the

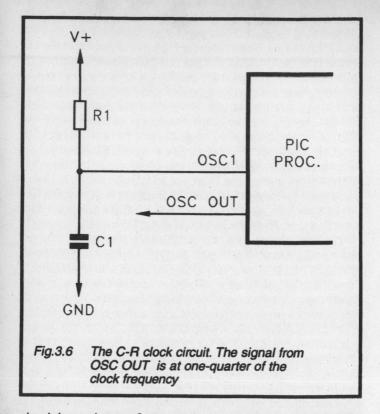

Fig.3.6 The C-R clock circuit. The signal from OSC OUT is at one-quarter of the clock frequency

circuit is running at a frequency in the megahertz range, and the stray capacitance then provides all the timing capacitance. This is not recommended by the manufacturer though, because results become very unpredictable. Also, temperature stability would be very poor indeed.

R1 should not have a value of less than 2k2 as this could result in the circuit failing to oscillate. Values of more than 1 megohm are not recommended as they leave the circuit vulnerable to problems with electrical noise and humidity. The recommended range of values for R1 is three kilohms to 100 kilohms. It is recommended that C1 should have a value of no less than 20 picofarads, and there is no upper limit on its value. I suppose that it would be possible to use an electrolytic capacitor (or another polarised type such as a tantalum bead capacitor) if the positive terminal is connected to R1 and the negative terminal is connected to the 0 volt supply rail. On the face of it there is no need to use a very high timing capacitance, but it should be borne in mind that there is no lower limit on the clock frequency when using a C-R clock oscillator. In some applications it is easier to use a very low clock frequency rather than the alternative of a high clock rate and numerous delaying loops in the software. The PIC processors that are intended for use with crystal clock circuits can also operate at very low frequencies provided they are used with an external clock generator circuit.

The PIC processors that have a window to permit erasure can be used with any of the four types of clock oscillator. The appropriate clock mode must be selected when the device is being programmed, and the programming software should make it easy to select the required mode. What the program is actually doing is programming a 4-bit register in the processor. This table shows the 4-bit binary code for each clock oscillator mode.

FOSC1	FOSC2	Oscillator mode
0	0	LP (low power crystal oscillator)
0	1	XT (Normal crystal or ceramic resonator)
1	0	HS (high speed crystal or resonator)
1	1	RC (C-R clock oscillator)

When using certain PIC processors that do not have the erasure window, it is essential to obtain the appropriate version for the type of clock oscillator that the system will utilise. The 16C54, 16C55, 16C56, and 16C57 all fall into this category. These processors have the oscillator bits pre-programmed at the factory, and can only be used with one type of clock oscillator circuit. The basic part number is the same for all versions, but a short suffix indicates the type of clock oscillator that each device requires. The table on page 70 should help to clarify matters.

Suffix	F.Min	F.Max	Notes
JW	DC	20MHz	Windowed device
XT	100kHz	4MHz	XT mode device
RC	DC	4MHz	RC mode device
LP	5kHz	100kHz	LP mode device
04	DC	4MHz	Any mode except HS
10	DC	10MHz	Any mode
20	DC	20MHz	Any mode

The 16C71 and 16C84 are not available in XT, RC, or LP versions, but are instead available in versions that can be programmed for operation in any mode. However, the suffix number indicates the maximum clock frequency in megahertz, and a 4MHz ('04') version is obviously unsuitable for operation in the HS mode.

Sleep Mode

One of the more unusual features of the PIC processors is the sleep mode. The processor is set into this mode using the special sleep instruction, and the device then largely shuts down. The point of doing this is that the processor consumes very little power when it is in the sleep mode, making it possible to use battery power even if the system will be left running for long periods. Obviously some means of breaking out of the sleep mode is required, and one way of achieving this is to pulse the MCLR input low. This resets the device, and it then starts running the program in EPROM in the normal way. With this method the processor remains in the standby mode until some external hardware detects that it is time for the system to start operating. This hardware then provides a reset pulse to MCLR, the processor runs its program and performs the necessary functions, and then goes into the sleep mode again. In this way the processor is only powered-up when there is something for it to do, and a very low average current consumption is obtained.

The processor can also be brought out of the sleep mode using a built-in timer called the watchdog timer. The general idea is to have the processor go into the sleep mode, and then after a period determined by the watchdog timer it wakes up and operates normally for a short time. Having done whatever needed to be done, or having discovered that there was nothing to do, the processor then goes back into the standby mode again. It continues in this fashion, and because it is in the sleep mode for a large percentage of the time it has a very low average current consumption. Of course, the processor does not totally shut down when it goes into the sleep mode, even though the clock oscillator stops. The watchdog timer has its own C-R oscillator so that it can continue to operate when the rest of the processor has shut down.

Another function of the watchdog timer is to periodically reset the processor. This facility is mainly used in applications where the system will be used in 'noisy' environments. Modern electronic circuits are very vulnerable to problems caused by the stray pickup of electrical noise and microprocessor based systems are more vulnerable than most. If an instruction, or possibly even if a piece of data, becomes corrupted, a microprocessor based system is almost certain to crash. Although the watchdog timer is set to periodically reset the system, the idea is that it should never actually reset the circuit in normal use. In the normal scheme of things the watchdog timer is always cleared before it has a chance to reset the system. The circuit therefore operates normally unless a crash occurs. Once the system has crashed, it is unlikely that the watchdog timer would be cleared, and before too long the watchdog timer would reset the system. While the system would not exactly carry on from where it left off, it would at least start from the beginning and would to some extent recover from the crash.

The watchdog timer consists of an 8-bit counter which is fed from a C-R oscillator, and it resets the processor after 256 input cycles. The watchdog timer can be used in conjunction with a prescaler, which is a divider circuit that can reduce the input frequency to the timer by factors of 2, 4, 8, 16, 32, 64, or 128. Without the prescaler a timeout occurs after about 18 milliseconds, but with the prescaler set for a division rate of 128 a timeout occurs after approximately 2.3 seconds.

Count On It
The PIC processors includes another timer, and this is also an 8-bit counter. It is possible to produce delays quite accurately

without the aid of a timer, but a timer provides what is usually a much easier way of handling things. This second timer is 'TMRO', and unlike the watchdog timer its input is fed from the system clock. However, it counts instruction cycles rather than clock cycles, and this means that the clock signal is divided by four prior to being fed to TMRO. If the processor has (say) a 4MHz clock, TMRO is incremented at 1MHz. This timer can also be used with the prescaler, which enables the input frequency to be reduced to as little as $\frac{1}{512}$th of the clock frequency. Although the prescaler can be used with TMRO or the watchdog timer, note that it can not be used with both of them at the same time.

Basically all the timer does is to start at zero, and increment by one each time an input pulse is received. Having reached a value of 255 (FF in hexadecimal) it cycles back to zero, and continues counting from there. It is up to the program to monitor the timer and take suitable action when the appropriate value is reached. In addition to counting clock cycles, the timer can also be set to count the pulses from an external circuit.

Protection
Unlike a straightforward EPROM, reading the contents of a PIC processor's EPROM is far from easy, and it probably requires some fairly advanced equipment to read the program contained in the EPROM. It can be done though. The PIC processors have a built-in 'fuse' which can be 'blown' during programming, and this renders the contents of the EPROM unreadable. The idea of this is to prevent anyone cloning one of your designs without your permission. Copying the hardware is easy enough, but without details of the program stored within the processor the gadget will do nothing at all. If you work long and hard on the software for a PIC project it makes sense to invoke the copy protection facility, unless you really do not care if others help themselves to your work. Of course, no copy protection device can ever provide 100 per cent reliable protection against copying, but this facility does at least make it extremely difficult for anyone to copy a program from a PIC device.

The Registers
The PIC processors use Harvard architecture, which means that

they have separate buses for data and instructions. The bus for data is an eight-bit type, but the bus for instructions is some 12 or 14 bits wide (depending on the complexity of the processor). Most processors have a common bus for fetching instructions and handling data, which is eight bits wide for the older processors, and 16 or 32 bits wide for the more recent offerings. This is known as Von Neumann architecture. There are definite benefits to Harvard architecture, and one of the main advantages is that one instruction can be executed while the next one is fetched. This internal 'multitasking' allied to some clever design enables most PIC instructions to be performed in a single clock cycle. In the Von Neumann architecture one instruction has to be performed before the next one can be fetched.

Although PIC processors have an instruction bus which is 12 or 14 bits wide, the data bus is only an eight-bit type, and these are therefore eight bit processors. As such they are not very powerful in some respects, but they are well suited to numerous everyday applications. The larger instruction bus does bring some advantage, since it enables all instructions to be coded into a single 12 or 14-bit word. With conventional eight-bit processors some instructions are two or even three bytes long, which tends to slow things down. Although PIC processors are in some ways quite simple, they are highly streamlined and operate at high speed.

In order to design PIC based systems you do not really need an in-depth understanding of the internal workings of the various PIC chips, but you do need to be familiar with the register set. The PIC register set is shown in Figure 3.7. The column of registers on the left are the ones in the data memory map, while those on the right are outside the memory map. If you are used to processors which have a combined data and instruction bus, you have to bear in mind here that these are the eight-bit registers which handle data. The 12 or 14 bit EPROM which contains the program instructions is entirely separate. The W register is the working register, and this is the PIC version of the accumulator. Most of the instructions make use of the W register, although in many cases there is the option of placing processed data somewhere other than in this register.

The bottom eight registers in the memory map have special

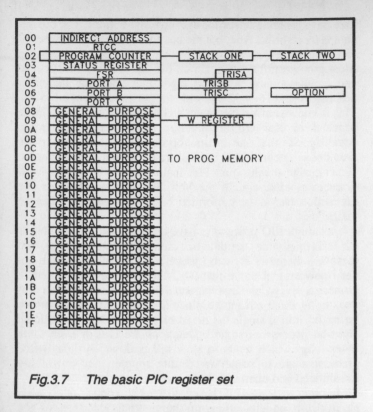

Fig.3.7   The basic PIC register set

functions, while those at higher addresses are general purpose file registers. The file registers are the RAM, and there can be anything from 25 to 232 of these. This is a list of the special function registers. I will adhere to the convention of using hexadecimal values for file register addresses. Note that some of the more upmarket PIC processors have additional special purpose registers.

Register   Function

00	Indirect Addressing
01	RTCC (real-time clock counter)
02	Program Counter

03	Status Register
04	Indirect Addressing
05	Port A
06	Port B
07	Port C (not implemented in all PIC processors)

It is necessary to have a good understanding of the way in which these registers operate, and we will therefore take a detailed look at each of them, starting with the ports. The ports are all bi-directional, with each line individually programmable as an input or an output. Ports A to C are respectively controlled by registers TRISA, TRISB, and TRISC. Of course, the 18 pin PIC processors do not have Port C, and therefore lack the TRISC register as well. Note that these registers are used to control the function of the port lines, and data for the ports is not written to these registers. The ports themselves are at file registers 05 to 07. The pins of Port A are named RA0 to RA3, and these correspond to bits 0 to 3 of file register 05. If Port A is used as outputs, and the binary value 00001100 is written to register 05, RA0 and RA1 are set low, while RA2 and RA3 are set high. Similarly, if Port A is used as four inputs, and RA0 plus RA1 are set low, and RA2 plus RA3 are set high, the binary value read from the port would be 00001100. The upper nibble of this register is unused, and the value written to these four bits has no affect on RA0 to RA3. When reading Port A, the upper four bits always return a value of zero.

Bits 0 to 3 of the TRISA register correspond to input/output terminals RA0 to RA3. Setting a bit at 1 results in the corresponding terminal of the chip acting as an input – setting a bit to 0 designates the corresponding terminal as an output. This 1 for 1nput and 0 for 0utput relationship is nice and easy to remember. At switch-on the lines of all ports are set as inputs. This is a standard safety measure with bi-directional computer ports, and it ensures that the system can not start off with two sets of outputs connected together (i.e. the computer port and the circuit which drives it). As a simple example of how TRISA is used, suppose that you wish to have RA0 as an input, and RA1 to RA3 as outputs. The binary code 00000001 (1 in hexadecimal or decimal) would be written to the TRISA register. The value written to the upper nibble is not important, but it is advisable to keep things simple and simply set these four bits at zero.

Port B is controlled in essentially the same manner, but via TRISB. All eight bits of this port are implemented. Data is written to or read from Port B via file register 6, and each bit of this register corresponds to one of the Port B input/output lines (RB0 to RB7). As before, setting a bit of the control register at 0 sets the corresponding line of the port as an output, setting a bit to 1 designed the line as an input. For example, to set the upper nibble as outputs and the lower nibble as inputs a binary value of 00001111 (15 in decimal, F in hexadecimal) would be written as TRISB. TRISC controls Port C (terminals RC0 to RC7) in exactly the same way. Data is written to or read from Port C via file register 7.

Status Symbols

As already explained, microprocessors have a status register which can supply useful snippets of information to your programs, and which are instrumental in most decision making instructions. File register 3 acts as the PIC status register, but only five bits operate as status flags. The three least significant bits are controlled by the arithmetic logic unit, and the next two bits provide reset information. Figure 3.8 shows the function of each bit in the status register, but this really requires some amplification.

Bit 0 is the standard carry/not borrow flag which is used by instructions that perform addition or subtraction, and by rotation instructions. Bit 1 is the digital carry flag (also known as an auxiliary carry flag), and this indicates if there is a carry from the low nibble of the arithmetic logic unit. The Z (zero) flag is at bit 2, and this is set to one when the result of an appropriate type of instruction is zero. The next two bits (3 and 4) are the PD (power down) and TO (time-out) flags. By testing these bits it is possible to determine whether a reset control has been produced by a watchdog timer timeout, a normal power-up, a wake-up from the Sleep mode by the watchdog timer, or a reset pulse on the MCLR terminal. Both of these flags are set to 1 when the chip is powered-up. The next table shows the affect of various types of reset on these two flags.

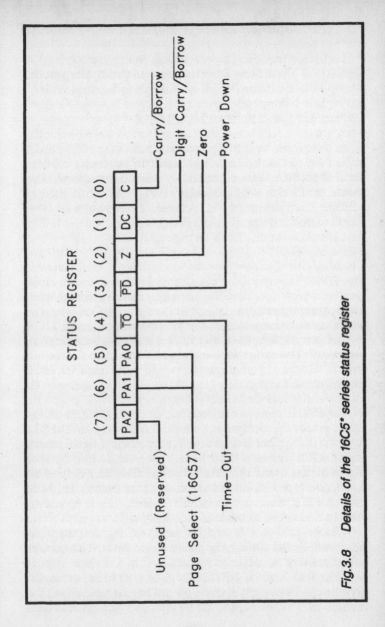

Fig.3.8   Details of the 16C5* series status register

TO	PD	Cause of Reset
0	0	Watchdog timer wake-up from Sleep mode
0	1	Watchdog timer timeout (not during Sleep mode)
1	0	Pulse on MCLR to wake-up from Sleep mode
1	1	Power-up
Unchanged		Reset pulse on MCLR input

In the more simple PIC processors such as the 16C54 bits 5 to 7 of the status register are general purpose read/write bits, but it is probably as well to simply leave them unused. This should ensure that your programs have upwards compatibility with the more advanced PIC processors. These bits do have functions on the more advanced PIC processors, and the 16C71 for example, uses bits 5 to 7 as page select bits.

Clocking On
The RTCC register (file register 1) is the real-time clock counter, which was described briefly earlier in this chapter. This register operates in conjunction with the OPTION register, which controls the prescaler. Only bits 0 to 5 of the OPTION register are implemented, and their functions are outlined in Figure 3.9. The names of some of these bits have changed in recent PIC data, so both names are provided in Figure 3.9. Most assemblers will accept either the old names or the new ones, or they can be accessed via their bit numbers.

The RTCC register can count either external pulses on the RTCC pin, or the clock signal after a division by four. Bit 5 of the OPTION register is used to select the required signal source for the RTCC register. If bit 5 is set to 0, the divided by four clock signal is used to increment the RTCC register. Setting bit 5 to 1 selects the RTCC pin as the input for the counter. Note that the RTCC pin must not be left 'floating' if it is unused. It must be tied to one or other of the supply rails.

Whichever source is used for the RTCC register, the input pulses will be fed through the prescaler. However, the prescaler can effectively be removed by setting it to a division rate of one. Bits 0 to 2 of the OPTION register control the prescaler, giving a choice of eight division rates. The next table shows the division rates available, and the bit settings which provide each

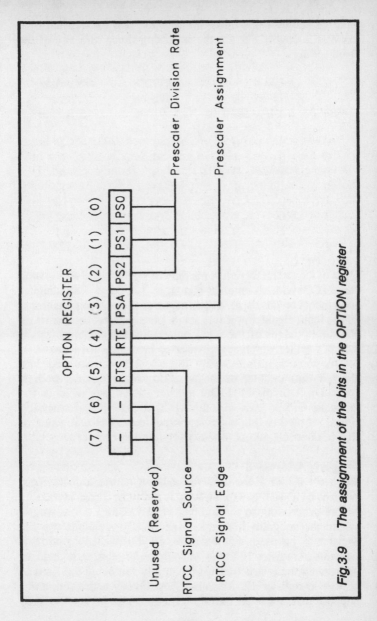

Fig.3.9   The assignment of the bits in the OPTION register

79

one. As show in this table, the division rate for the real-time counter is double that for the watchdog timer with any of the 8-bit settings.

Option Register			RTCC Division	Watchdog Timer Division
Bit 2	Bit 1	Bit 0		
0	0	0	2	1
0	0	1	4	2
0	1	0	8	4
0	1	1	16	8
1	0	0	32	16
1	0	1	64	32
1	1	0	128	64
1	1	1	256	128

Bit 4 of the OPTION register is only of significance when using the RTCC with an external signal. If it is set to 0 the counter increments on the rising edges (negative to positive transitions) of the input signal, but if it is set to 1 the counter increments on the falling edges of the input pulses. In many applications it will not matter which edge is used to increment the counter.

As pointed out previously, the prescaler can be used with the real-time counter or the watchdog timer, but not both at once. Bit 3 of the OPTION register determines whether the prescaler will be used with the RTCC register or the watchdog timer. Set bit 3 to 0 to direct its output to the RTCC register, or to 1 to direct its output to the watchdog timer.

Properly Addressed

Registers 0 and 4 are used for indirect addressing. It would perhaps be as well to explain what is meant by direct addressing before proceeding to the indirect variety. Direct addressing is where the program instruction specifically mentions the file register to be used. For example, if you needed to add the contents of register 12 to the value in the W register, with direct addressing the instruction would simply run along the lines of add W to register 12. Register 12 is directly addressed, and I suppose that in a sense the W register has also been selected by a form of direct addressing. The W register is a special case though, and its use is implicit in most instructions.

Indirect addressing operates in a manner that is almost as simple as direct addressing. The address of the file to be used is placed in file register 4, which is called the file select register (FSR). The data for the selected register is written to register 0, the indirect address register. For example, if a value of 15 is placed in register 4, and a value of 11 is then written to register 0, the value of 11 will actually be placed in register 15 (i.e. the register pointed to by the address in register 4). Register 0 does not actually exist, but using indirect addressing the value of 11 can still be read back from register 0. However, it is really register 15 that is being read and not register 0. Things would go awry if a value of zero was written to the FSR, setting register 0 as the one selected for indirect addressing. Data written to register 0 would go nowhere, and any data read back from register 0 would always be zero. Indirect addressing may seem to be of limited value, but it can be useful in conjunction with a program loop. The value in the FSR can be incremented or decremented on each loop, so that data can be quickly written to a block of registers.

PC and Stack

The program counter (register 2) is a 9-bit type on the 16C54, and it generates addresses for the program store (the EPROM or EEPROM). Once again, you have to bear in mind that the program instructions and the data are carried on separate buses, and be careful not to confuse program addresses and register file addresses. As the program counter is a 9-bit type, it gives an address range of 000 to 1FF in hexadecimal, or 0 to 511 in decimal numbering. On power-up or after a reset the program counter is set at 1FF (hexadecimal), and it is then automatically incremented during the execution of each program instruction unless that instruction changes the counter. It is possible to change the program counter by writing data to it, but only the lower eight bits can be controlled in this way. Writing data to the program counter results in the most significant bit being set to 0. Directly controlling the program counter is strictly for those who know exactly what they are doing.

There are other instructions that will alter the program counter's contents, and break it out of its normal incremental mode. A GOTO instruction permits all nine bits of the counter to be loaded with the required address. With a CALL instruction the lower eight bits are loaded directly, and the most significant bit is cleared (set to 0). CALLed subroutines are therefore limited to the lower half of the address range. The return from subroutine instruction (RETLW) causes the program counter to be loaded from the top of the Stack, which is where the contents of the program counter were stored when the CALL instruction invoked the subroutine. This instruction also returns a value which is placed in the W register. Some PIC processors (but not the 16C5* series) have a RETURN instruction, which is essentially the same as the RETLW instruction, but it does not return a value.

Some PIC devices (but again, not the 16C5* series) implement interrupts, and have a return from interrupt instruction. This is the RETFIE instruction, and it operates in a similar manner to RETLW and RETURN. The interrupt causes the contents of the program counter to be stored on the top of the Stack, and sets the Global Interrupt Enable bit to prevent further interrupts until the current one has been completed. The return from interrupt instruction resets the Global Interrupt Enable bit and loads the program counter from the top of the Stack.

Exceptions

This description of the PIC processors has necessarily been rather generalised. Some PIC devices are more sophisticated than others, and the descriptions provided here have been largely based on the simpler processors which are easier to understand, and represent the best starting point. It is well worth taking a quick look at one of the more recent PIC processors, and the 16C71 represents one of the more interesting of these. This device has 1K × 14 bits of EPROM, and 36 bytes of RAM. The most obvious way in which this differs from the more simple devices such as the 16C54 is that it has a built-in 8-bit analogue to digital converter, plus a multiplexer which provides four analogue inputs. Due to the inclusion of the analogue converter, and because there are other

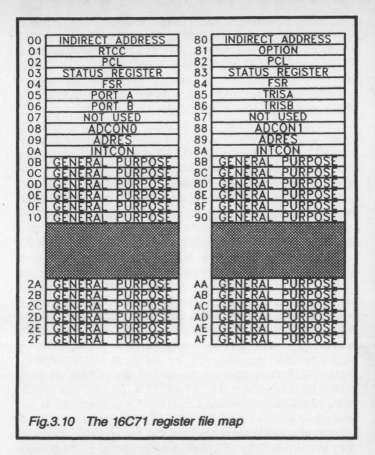

00	INDIRECT ADDRESS	80	INDIRECT ADDRESS
01	RTCC	81	OPTION
02	PCL	82	PCL
03	STATUS REGISTER	83	STATUS REGISTER
04	FSR	84	FSR
05	PORT A	85	TRISA
06	PORT B	86	TRISB
07	NOT USED	87	NOT USED
08	ADCON0	88	ADCON1
09	ADRES	89	ADRES
0A	INTCON	8A	INTCON
0B	GENERAL PURPOSE	8B	GENERAL PURPOSE
0C	GENERAL PURPOSE	8C	GENERAL PURPOSE
0D	GENERAL PURPOSE	8D	GENERAL PURPOSE
0E	GENERAL PURPOSE	8E	GENERAL PURPOSE
0F	GENERAL PURPOSE	8F	GENERAL PURPOSE
10	GENERAL PURPOSE	90	GENERAL PURPOSE
2A	GENERAL PURPOSE	AA	GENERAL PURPOSE
2B	GENERAL PURPOSE	AB	GENERAL PURPOSE
2C	GENERAL PURPOSE	AC	GENERAL PURPOSE
2D	GENERAL PURPOSE	AD	GENERAL PURPOSE
2E	GENERAL PURPOSE	AE	GENERAL PURPOSE
2F	GENERAL PURPOSE	AF	GENERAL PURPOSE

Fig.3.10 The 16C71 register file map

aspects of the chip which differ from the 16C5* series, it has the modified register file map of Figure 3.10.

There is clearly a major change here in that there are two pages of registers, and bit 5 of the status register permits switching between the two. This is set to 0 to select page 0, or to 1 to select page 1. The 12 lowest registers are special purpose types, and some have the same function in both pages. These can therefore be accessed with either page 0 or page 1 selected, as can the 36 general purpose registers. Some of the special function registers have different functions in the two pages, such as the input/output port registers. In page 0 these registers give direct access to the input/output pins in the normal way, but with page 1 selected the port direction control registers (TRISA and TRISB) are available instead. This gives access to the port control registers without having to use special instructions. Instead, page 1 is selected and data is written to these register files in the normal way.

A/D Conversion

Special purpose registers ADCON0 and ADCON1 provide a number of control and status bits associated with the analogue to digital converter. Before considering the 16C71's analogue converter in detail, it would perhaps be as well to cover some basics of analogue to digital conversion. Computers work with 1s and 0s, but in the real world anything measurable can have an infinite range of values. With something like an analogue test meter there might be a voltage range which covers potentials in the range 0 to 10 volts, and in theory the meter would be able to measure any voltage in that range. It would certainly produce a reading for any voltage in the range 0 to 10 volts, but how accurate would that meter reading actually be? No matter how accurately the unit was built and set up, there would still be a limit on the resolution of the readings. This is simply because the pointer of the meter can not be infinitely narrow, and there can not be an infinite number of scale markings. If an input voltage of 4.123456789 volts was applied to the meter, the user would at best be able to interpret this as a reading of a little over 4.1 volts. Although there is an infinite number of possible input voltages, and even minute changes in the measured voltage will produce some change in the position of the pointer, there are practical limits on the accuracy of an analogue measuring system.

A digital measuring system can only distinguish between a certain number of input levels, and on the face of it a digital system is less precise than an analogue system. In reality a digital system often offers better accuracy than an analogue equivalent. If we return to our voltmeter example, an equivalent digital multimeter would typically have a three and a half digit display with a measuring range of 0 to 19.99 volts. This gives a basic resolution of 0.01 volts (10 millivolts). If the actual input voltage was 5.007 volts, the meter's display would read 5.01 volts, which is as near to the true voltage as its display permits. This reading is clearly an approximation of the true input voltage, but provided the resolution of the system is high enough, this does not matter. The readings obtained will be close enough to the true input levels, and the system will tell the user what he or she needs to know. In this example the input voltage can be read to the nearest 0.01 volts, which actually represents about 10 times the effective resolution of most analogue meters!

The built-in analogue to digital converter of the 16C71 is successive approximation type which offers 8-bit resolution. Returned values will therefore be in the range 0 to 255. This gives slightly better resolution than a two and a half digit display, and in this respect the resolution is somewhat inferior to those of a typical digital display. However, the accuracy of readings is at least equal to those obtained from a good analogue display, and they are perfectly adequate for many applications. The converter is a linear type, which means that if a reading of (say) 250 was obtained with an input potential of 5 volts, readings of 100 and 50 would be obtained at input voltages of two volts and one volt.

Figure 3.11 outlines the functions of the bits in the ADCON0 and ADCON1 registers, but note that only two bits of ADCON1 are actually used. These are the two least significant bits, which are designated PCF0 and PCF1. These control inputs RA0 to RA3, and determine whether they function as normal digital inputs or as analogue inputs. There are four operations, as follows:

PCFG1	PCFG0	RA0/1	RA2	RA3
0	0	Analogue	Analogue	Analogue
0	1	Analogue	Analogue	Ref. Input
1	0	Analogue	Digital	Digital
1	1	Digital	Digital	Digital

This arrangement permits the device to operate with four analogue inputs, four digital inputs, or two of each type. Normally the full scale sensitivity of the analogue converter is equal to the positive supply rail (VDD), but there is the option

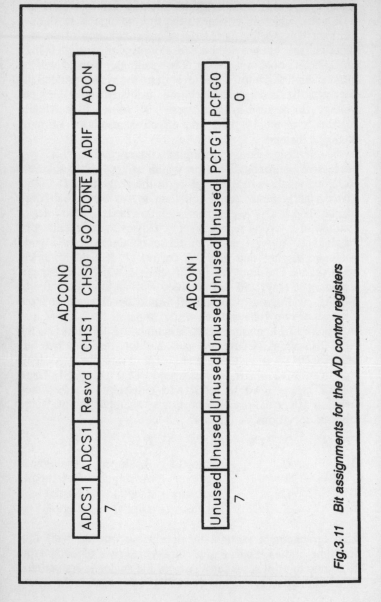

Fig.3.11 Bit assignments for the A/D control registers

of having RA0 to RA2 as analogue inputs, and the full scale sensitivity equal to a potential applied to RA3.

Apart from bit 5, all the bits of ADCON0 have functions. The converter is switched on and off using bit 0. Setting this bit at 0 switches on the converter, and setting it to 1 switches it on. When switched off it is not merely disconnected from the input pins, but it is totally shut down and consumes no significant power. Bit 1 is the conversion completed interrupt flag. This is set to 1 when a conversion has been completed, and is cleared by the software. To start a conversion bit 2 is set to 1, and it is automatically reset by the hardware when the conversion has been completed. The required analogue channel is selected using bits 3 and 4, and this operates in the manner shown in this table.

CHS1	CHS0	Channel Selected
0	0	0
0	1	1
1	0	2
1	1	3

Bits 6 and 7 are used to select the clock source for the analogue to digital converter, and there are four choices. The system clock can be used with division rates of 2, 8, or 32, or an internal C-R clock oscillator can be selected. This table shows how to select the required clock source.

ADCS1	ADCS0	Clock Source
0	0	½ System Clock
0	1	⅛ System Clock
1	0	1/32 System Clock
1	1	Internal C-R Oscillator

The clock period for the converter must not be less than two microseconds, which means that the clock frequency must be no more than 500kHz. Each conversion takes 10 clock cycles, which gives a minimum conversion time of 20 microseconds. This equates to a maximum of 50,000 conversions per second. In practice it would probably not be possible to quite achieve this rate, but the conversion rate is more than adequate for most purposes. The internal C-R clock provides a clock period of between two and six microseconds (typically four microseconds), and this can be useful if a high conversion rate is needed but the system clock frequency is relatively low. Note that the internal clock oscillator is not very stable, and its frequency varies considerably with changes in supply voltage and temperature.

In order to take a reading from the analogue to digital converter, ADCON1 must first be set to give the desired input configuration. Then ADCON0 must be set up correctly, which requires three parameters to be set. Select the required clock source, select the desired channel, and turn on the analogue to digital converter. If converter generated interrupts are going to be used, the appropriate bits should be set up next, but in most cases the converter will probably not be used in conjunction with interrupts. The chip is then ready for a reading to be taken. To take a conversion the GO/DONE bit is set to 1, and the converter can then be read after a suitable delay. This delay can be provided by a timing loop or by using a loop to monitor an appropriate status flag.

The 16C71 has other differences to the 16C54, such as an eight-deep Stack rather than a two-deep type. This gives more scope for using sub-routines, and also for using interrupts that are supported by the 16C71 but not the 16C54. For beginners the most simple of the PIC processors, such as the 16C54, represent the best starting point. Before too long you will probably want to try the more sophisticated devices, which open up new possibilities. You will certainly need to obtain either some data sheets for the PIC processors, or (preferably) the full Microchip Data Book.

Points to Remember

The PIC microcontrollers use Harvard architecture, which means that they have separate buses for data and instructions. The ROM holds instructions, and the RAM is used for data.

PIC software is normally written in assembly language. You are still programming the chip using its instruction set, but the assembler program works out the binary codes for you and provides other help.

In order to program PIC chips you need a suitable development or programming system that should include an assembler, the programming software and hardware, plus (probably) some form of PIC simulator or emulator.

Make sure that you obtain a development or programmer system that supports the PIC devices you intend to use. The more devices the system supports the more use it is likely to be.

The re-programmable chips are mostly erased using a special ultra-violet light-box which must have the right type of fluorescent tube. The 16C84 has EEROM which can be erased electronically.

You must be careful to use the version of a processor that supports the type of clock circuit you will be using. Where appropriate, you must program the chip to use the right type of clock circuit.

Use a crystal controlled clock where either very fast operation (over 4MHz) or good timing accuracy is required.

There is no lower limit on the clock frequency if a C-R clock oscillator or an external type is used.

Each line of a PIC port can be set as an input or an output via the appropriate control register (TRISA for Port A, TRISB for Port B, etc.).

The built-in timer (RTCC) can be used to count external pulses or the divided by four system clock.

The Status register contains flag bits that indicate the result of some instructions (e.g. carry and zero bits), and these can be used in conditional instructions.

The watchdog timer can be used to reset the processor or wake it up from SLEEP mode. Both timers can be used in conjunction with a programmable prescaler (divider) circuit.

The OPTION register is a control register that is outside the data memory map. It is mainly used to control the timers and the prescaler.

The Stack is loaded with the address of the last instruction when the program goes into a subroutine. Once the subroutine has been completed the address in the Stack is incremented by one and loaded into the program counter. This enables the program to carry on where it left off. You do not control the Stack – the processor handles the loading and unloading of the Stack automatically.

The program counter can be read and altered by the program, but it is not normally necessary to do so.

Start with the more basic PIC chips such as the 16C54, and progress to the more interesting devices such as the 16C71 when you have gained some experience with the simple processors.

Chapter 4

THE INSTRUCTION SET

A PIC processor, in common with all microprocessors, requires instructions that are in the form of binary numbers. While it is not impossible to work out a program in this machine code as it is called, it is very time consuming to look up all the codes and put together a complete program. Also, with most programs it is necessary to loop back or jump forward to specific points in the program. You could keep a list of the addresses of the points in the program that you need to loop or jump to, but this can get very confusing as it is difficult to remember which address is which. Programs for PIC based systems are normally written in assembly language, and this is very much easier than writing programs in pure machine code. Assembly language is not a high level language such as BASIC where you write programs using what is virtually plain English. Neither does assembly language take a single program instruction and then convert it into several machine code instructions. With a high level language it is quite normal for each program instruction to end up as dozens of instructions at the microprocessor. With assembly language you take things one step at a time, and each instruction that you give the assembler is converted into a single machine code instruction.

So just what does an assembler do? By using mnemonics for machine code instructions it becomes much easier to write programs. In order to clear the contents of the working register for example, the mnemonic CLRW would be used. This is much easier to remember than a binary number some 12 or 14 digits long. At first it might be necessary to keep looking up the mnemonics for the instructions you require, but you soon find that you have learned them all. Life is made much easier for PIC programmers by the relatively small number of instructions that are implemented. Committing the full instruction set to memory only involves learning about three dozen instructions.

An important feature of assemblers is their support for 'labels'. A label is simply a name that can be used at any point in a program, and then used to return to that point using the label rather than the address it represents. There may be a limit of eight characters in the label (some assemblers allow long names though), but even eight characters is sufficient to enable meaningful names to be used. For example, if a section of the program is used to flash a LED indicator on and off, the first address in the routine could be called 'LEDFLASH'.

When writing an assembly language program you do not produce one long string of text. The assembler requires the program in the form of one line of text per instruction. Each line of text has to be set out in the correct fashion, which means organizing the instructions in fields. There are usually four fields, which basically just means that the instructions are laid out in four columns. The first column contains the label, but this field is blank for many instructions as labels are only used where they are really needed. The next column contains the mnemonics for the instructions, and the third field contains any additional data needed in the instruction. Finally, the fourth field is used for any comments the programmer may wish to include. These comments are purely optional, and the fourth column can be left totally blank if desired. However, bear in mind that assembly language is not easy to follow even if you are an expert programmer. While every step of the program may be clear in your mind at the time you write the code, the function of each program line might be far less obvious a week later. After a month or two you might have largely forgotten what the program does, and could have no idea how it actually does it. A short comment for each instruction can make the program much easier to follow if you return to it at a later date.

The example instructions shown on page 93 show how things are organized.

The first four program lines set up Port B as eight inputs, and Port A as four outputs. Any setting up of this type is normally done at the beginning of the program rather than waiting until the last possible moment. Having everything of this type at the beginning makes it easy to troubleshoot on a faulty program, and to modify an existing program to suit a new application. Also, it is generally better to get this type of thing out of the way before getting into the main program where the time taken to set things up could be unhelpful. The MOVLW instruction moves the operand (255 decimal – 11111111 in binary) into the W register. The next instruction moves the contents of the W register into TRISB, and this sets all the Port B lines as inputs. Next the W register is cleared (all bits are set to zero), and this value is transferred to TRISA to set all the lines of Port A as outputs. The beginning of this routine has been given the label 'START', but this is actually superfluous as the program never branches back to this point. On the other hand, the label will not impair the operation of the assembler or the assembled program in any way.

Field 1 Label	Field 2 Mnemonic	Field 3 Operand	Field 4 Comment
START	MOVLW	255	Loads 255 into W register
	TRIS	B	Sets Port B as inputs
	CLRW		W register set to zero
	TRIS	A	Sets Port A as outputs
	MOVLW	100	Number of loops
	MOVWF	12	Register 12 keeps count
LOOP	DECFSZ	12,1	Decrement register 12, jump if 0
	GOTO	LOOP	Loop until register 12 = 0
LOOP2	NOP		
	GOTO	LOOP2	Loop indefinitely
	END		

The next four program lines form a simple loop, and the idea is for the program to loop 100 times before the program continues. First a value of 100 is placed in the W register, and then this value is transferred to register file 12. The next instruction decrements the contents of register 12 (i.e. reduces it from 100 to 99), and the next instruction simply loops the program back one instruction. This makes use of the 'LOOP' label to define the loop point. The program keeps looping around these two lines until the value in register file 12 equals zero. The DECFSZ instruction then detects that the result of the calculation is zero, and jumps over the next instruction. This breaks the program out of the loop. An 'empty' loop of this type does not actually do anything, but it can still be useful where a delay is required. The loop can be made to perform one or more actions the required number of times by adding suitable instructions between the beginning and the end of the loop. When using loops make sure that you loop the program back to the correct instruction. In this case the MOVLW instruction is at the beginning of the loop routine, but the program must not be looped back to there. This would keep resetting the value in file register 12 to 100. This would prevent it from ever reaching zero, and the program would loop indefinitely.

An indefinite loop is the action provided by the final two lines of the program. In most applications the program will perform various loops, and will never come to an end. It is unusual to have an application where the system is switched on, it performs some function or other, and then needs to do nothing more until it is turned off and then switched on again. However, if you do design a system for an application of this type, you should not simply let the processor run out of instructions, as this could give unpredictable results. There are various ways of bringing things to a predictable end, and the most simple is to put the program into an endless loop, as in this example. Another option is to use some hardware and suitable software to make the system switch itself off. The program finishes with an END instruction, which simply indicates to the assembler that the end of the program has been reached. Without an END instruction the assembler will probably produce an error message, but it would probably assemble the program correctly anyway.

Although this example program does not actually do anything worthwhile, it does demonstrate the basics of assembly language programming. You will note that most instructions have an operand in field three (i.e. data of some kind or a data address that the instruction requires), but not all instructions do so. In this program the CLRW instruction does not require an operand, since it only operates on the W register, and can only set it to one value (zero). A number of instructions require two operands. On the face of it only one operand is needed, and this is the address of the register file which must be decremented. However, the DECFSZ instruction, and many others, can place the result in either a register file or in the W register. The second operand is either 0 or 1, and these respectively direct the result of the instruction to the W register or the file register. The second operand is really just a simple switch that selects one of two possible destinations for the result.

A few instructions require two 'proper' operands, and this is where the instruction must include both the address of a register file and a value to be operated on. This is an example of such an instruction:

$$BSF \quad 15,2$$

This instruction sets the specified bit of a register to 1. In this example the register is register file 15, and it is bit 2 that is set to 1.

The Instruction Set

Although the PIC processors are of the RISC variety, they still have some 35 or more instructions with which budding programmers have to be familiar. Unless you have a particularly good memory it is probably not worthwhile trying to memorise all of the instructions before you start writing some initial exercise programs. On the other hand, you need to be reasonably familiar with the basic capabilities of the PIC processors, and as a bare minimum you need to read through the following description of the instruction set at least two or three times. You will soon become more familiar with the available instructions once you start writing programs. Initially you must expect to get stuck occasionally, and have to refer to the list of instructions to find one that will provide the function you require. With any microprocessor, but particularly with RISC types, you must bear in mind that each instruction is quite basic and that many simple tasks will require a short series of instructions.

This description of the instruction set has been kept as brief and simple as possible. Information such as the binary code for each instruction has not been included as it is not the sort of thing that is normally needed when designing PIC based systems. The assembler produces the binary codes and it is the mnemonics that the programmer must be familiar with. The PIC processor databook contains all the binary codes for the instructions if you should need them for some reason. As pointed out previously, the instruction sets vary slightly from one PIC processor to another. Rather than try to give all the instructions for all the processors, which would tend to be confusing, the full instruction set for one processor is described. This processor is the 16C71, which has basically the same instruction set (but different binary coding) as the 16C5* series of microcontrollers. However, the 16C5* series lack the ADDLW, SUBLW, RETURN, and RETFIE instructions. Obviously the 16C5* series and the 16C71 are largely compatible, and if you can write assembly language programs for one there should be no difficulty in writing software for the other.

The descriptions of some instructions are a bit sketchy, but this is due to the fact that detailed descriptions of what is happening are provided elsewhere in this book. For instance, detailed descriptions of bitwise processes and rotations are not described in detail here, as they are described in detail in Chapter 2. The purpose of this chapter is to act as a handy reference source which provides brief but concise information on the full 16C71 instruction set. The basic format is the same for each instruction, with a description of the basic function provided, followed by details of the assembly language syntax, the status flags that are affected, the number of cycles the instruction takes, and the number of words. Finally, one or two examples are used to show the precise function of the instruction.

These conventions are used in the syntax examples:

Letter	Meaning
b	Bit number in file (0 to 7)
d	Direction flag (0 = result in W register, 1 = result in file)
f	File register address
k	8-bit constant
kk	9-bit constant

ADDLW

The value in the W register is added to the literal k (i.e. the value in the W register is added to the value contained in the instruction in k). The result is stored in the W register.

Syntax	ADDLW	k
Status	C,DC,Z	
Cycles	1	
Words	1	

Example ADDLW 12

12 is added to the contents of the W register.
If W = 14 initially, after the instruction it will equal 26.

ADWF

This instruction adds the contents of the W register to the file register F. The latter can be a numbered or a named file. The result is stored in the W register if d is 0, or in register F if d is 1.

Syntax	ADDWF	f,d
Status	C,DC,Z	
Cycles	1	
Words	1	

Example 1 ADDWF 18,0

The contents of the W register are added to file 18 and the result is stored in the W register.
If W = 23 and file 18 = 11, after the instruction W = 34 and file 18 = 11.

Example 2 ADDWF 18,1

The contents of the W register are added to file 18 and the result is stored in file 18.
If W = 23 and file 18 = 11, after the instruction W = 23 and file 18 = 34.

ANDLW

The contents of the W register are bitwise ANDed with the 8-bit literal value k (i.e. the value included in the instruction). The result is stored in the W register.

Syntax	ANDLW	k
Status	Z	

Cycles	1
Words	1

Example   ANDLW   10101010
         The contents of the W register are bitwise ANDed
         with the 8-bit value 10101010, and the returned
         value is placed back in the W register.
         If the W register initially contains the binary value
         11110000, after the instruction it will contain
         10100000.

ANDWF

The contents of the W register are bitwise ANDed with the
value stored in file F. If d = 0 the returned value is placed in the
W register. The result is placed in register file F if d = 1.

Syntax	ANDWF f,d
Status	Z
Cycles	1
Words	1

Example 1 ANDWF   18,0
         The contents of the W register are bitwise ANDed
         with the value in file register 18, and the result is
         stored in the W register.
         If the W register contains 10101010 and file
         register 18 contains 11110000, after the instruction
         the W register is set to 10100000 and file register
         18 remains at 11110000.

Example 2 ANDWF   18,1
         The same as example 1, but the W register is not
         changed by this instruction, and the result is placed
         in file register 18.

BCF

This instruction simply clears (sets to zero) the specified bit (b)
of the specified register (f).

Syntax	BFCF	f,b
Status	–	
Cycles	1	
Words	1	

Example   BCF   11,2
           If file register 11 is initially at a value of 00001111,
           after this instruction it will contain 00001011.

BSF

This instruction sets (to 1) the specified bit of the specified register.

Syntax	BSF	f,b
Status	–	
Cycles	1	
Words	1	

Example   BSF   11,2
           If file register 11 is initially at a value of 11110000,
           after this instruction it will contain 11110100.

BTFC

If the specified bit (b) of the specified register file (f) is clear (set at 0), the next instruction is skipped. Strictly speaking the program does not skip straight over the next instruction, but instead replaces it with a NOP (no operation) instruction. This gives a delay of one clock cycle before the next instruction is reached.

Syntax	BTFC	f,b
Status	–	
Cycles	1 (or 2 if skip performed)	
Words	1	

Example   BTFC   15,1
           If bit 1 of file register 15 is clear (0), the next
           instruction is replaced with a NOP instruction.

If bit 1 of file register 8 is set (1), the next
instruction is performed normally.

BTFSS

If the specified bit (b) of the specified register file (f) is set (1),
the next instruction is replaced with a NOP instruction. This
effectively skips the next instruction, but note that the NOP
instruction it is replaced by takes one clock cycle.

Syntax	BTFSS f,b
Status	–
Cycles	1 (or 2 if skip performed)
Words	1

Example   BTFSS   15,1
            If bit 1 of file register 15 is set (1), the next
            instruction is replaced with a NOP instruction.
            If bit 1 of file register 15 is clear (0), the program
            continues normally.

CALL

This instruction is used to call a subroutine. The current address
in the program counter is incremented by one and pushed onto
the Stack, and the program counter is then loaded with address
'K'. The program then continues executing from address 'K'.
The limit on address 'K' is eight bits, which means that the
subroutine must start within the first 256 bytes of code.

Syntax	CALL K
Status	–
Cycles	2
Words	1

Example   CALL   SENSORS
            The program jumps to the address assigned to
            'SENSORS' and starts executing from there.

CLRF

The specified file register is cleared (i.e. all bits are set to 0) and the Z flag is set.

Syntax	CLRF	f
Status	Z	
Cycles	1	
Words	1	

Example   CLRF   12
All the bits in file register 12 are set to 0.

CLRW

Clears all the bits of the W register to zero and sets the Z flag to 1.

Syntax	CLRW
Status	Z
Cycles	1
Words	1

Example   CLRW
Sets all the bits of the W register to 0 regardless of their previous state, and sets the Z flag to 1.

CLRWDT

This instruction clears the watchdog timer and prescaler of the watchdog timer. It also sets status bits TO and PD.

Syntax	CLRWDT
Status	TO, PD
Cycles	1
Words	1

Example   CLRWDT
All bits of the watchdog timer and prescaler are at 0 after this instruction has been completed. The TO and PD status bits are set.

COMF

The contents of the specified register are complemented (i.e. 1s are set to 0, and 0s are set to 1). The result is placed in the specified register if d = 1, or in the W register if d = 0.

Syntax   COMF   f,d
Status   Z
Cycles   1
Words   1

Example 1 COMF   12,1
         The contents of file register 12 are complemented. If register 12 contained 11110000 before the instruction, it would contain 00001111 afterwards.

Example 2 COMF   12,0
         The value in file register 12 is complemented and stored in the W register. If file register 12 contained 11110000 before the instruction, it would still contain this value afterwards, but a value of 00001111 would be placed in the W register.

DECF

The specified register is decremented by one. If d = 1 the result is placed in the specified register, or it is placed in the W register if d = 0.

Syntax   DECF   f,d
Status   Z
Cycles   1
Words   1

Example 1 DECF   14,1
         The contents of file register 14 are decremented by one and the result is placed back in register 14. If the value in register 14 was originally 11110001, after the instruction it will be 11110000.

Example 2 DECF   14,0

The contents of register 14 are decremented by one, and the result is placed in the W register. If register 14 contained the value 11110001 before the instruction, it would still contain this value afterwards. The W register would be set at 11110000.

DECFSZ

Like the DDECF instruction, the specified register is decremented by one. If d = 1 the result is placed in the specified register, or it is placed in the W register if d = 0. Additionally, if the result is 0 the next instruction is replaced with a NOP (no operation) instruction.

Syntax	DECF	f,d
Status	Z	
Cycles	1	
Words	1 (2 if skip performed)	

Example 1 DECF   14,1
> The contents of file register 14 are decremented by one and the result is placed back in register 14. If the value in register 14 was originally 11110001, after the instruction it will be 11110000. The next instruction is performed normally.

Example 2 DECF   14,0
> The contents of register 14 are decremented by one, and the result is placed in the W register. If register 14 contained the value 00000001 before the instruction, it would still contain this value afterwards. The W register would be set at 00000000. The next instruction would then be replaced by a NOP instruction, effectively skipping over it.

GOTO

This is the unconditional branch instruction. The program goes to the specified address and continues to operate from there.

Syntax	GOTO	k
Status	–	
Cycles	2	
Words	1	

Example GOTO   PROG2

The program goes to the address assigned to label 'PROG2', and continues at this address.

INCF

The contents of the specified register are incremented by one, and the result is placed back in that register if $d = 1$, or in the W register if $d = 0$.

Syntax	INCF	f,d
Status	Z	
Cycles	1	
Words	1	

Example 1 INCF   12,0

The value in file register 12 is incremented by one and placed in the W register. The contents of register 12 are not altered by this instruction. If file register 12 contained a value of 15, after this instruction it would still contain a value of 15, but the W register would be set to 16..

Example 2 INCF   12,1

The value in file register 12 is incremented by one and stored back in that register. The W register is unaffected by this instruction.

INCFSZ

The specified file register is incremented by one and the result is placed in that register if $d = 1$, or in the W register if $d = 0$. Additionally, if the result equals 0 the next instruction is replaced with a NOP instruction, and is effectively skipped.

Syntax	INCFSZ	f,d
Status	–	
Cycles	1 (or 2 if skip performed)	
Words	1	

Example 1 INCFSZ   14,1

The contents of file register 14 are incremented by one, and the result is placed back in that register. If register 14 originally contained a value of 27, it would contain 28 after this instruction. The next instruction would not be skipped.

Example 2 INCFSZ   14,0

The contents of file register 14 are incremented by one, and the result is placed in the W register. If register 14 contained a value of 11111111, this would be incremented to 00000000 and loaded into the W register. Register 14 would still be set at 11111111. As the result of this instruction is zero, the next instruction would be replaced by a NOP instruction.

IORLW

The contents of the W register are bitwise ORed with the 8-bit literal 'k' (i.e. the 8-bit value contained in the instruction). The result of this instruction is placed in the W register.

Syntax	IORLW	k
Status	Z	
Cycles	1	
Words	1	

Example   IORLW   15

If the W register contains the binary value 01010101 before this instruction is performed, it will contain the binary code 01011111 afterwards (i.e. the result of bitwise ORing 00001111 and 01010101).

IORWF

The contents of the W register are bitwise ORed with the contents of the specified register. If d = 0 the result is stored in the W register, but if d = 1 the result is stored back in the specified register.

Syntax	IORWF f,d
Status	Z
Cycles	1
Words	1

Example 1 IORWF 15,0

The contents of the W register are bitwise ORed with the value in file register 15. If the W register and file register 15 respectively contain 01010101 and 00001111, the result of 01011111 will be stored in the W register. The contents of register 15 would be unaffected by this instruction.

Example 2 IORWF 15,1

The same as example 1, but the result is stored in register 15 and the contents of the W register are unaffected.

MOVLW

This instruction moves the 8-bit literal 'k' (i.e. the value provided within the instruction) into the W register.

Syntax	MOVLW k
Status	–
Cycles	1
Words	1

Example MOVLW 56

A value of 56 is loaded into the W register.

MOVF

The contents of the specified register are moved to either the W register (if d = 0) or back to the specified register (d = 1). Although, on the face of it, using this instruction with d = 1 has no affect, it can be useful to test the contents of a register, with the Z flag indicating the result.

Syntax	MOVF	f,d
Status	Z	
Cycles	1	
Words	1	

Example   MOVF   15,0
The contents of file register 15 are loaded into the W register. The value in register 15 remains unaltered.

MOVWF

This instruction moves the contents of the W register to the specified register.

Syntax	MOVWF	f
Status	–	
Cycles	1	
Words	1	

Example   MOVWF 49
Moves the value stored in the W register to file register 49. The value in the W register is not altered by this instruction – it is simply copied to register 49.

NOP

This is the no operation instruction, which does absolutely nothing. It simply provides a delay of one clock cycle.

Syntax	NOP
Status	–
Cycles	1
Words	1

Example   NOP
          Has no effect on any registers.

RETFIE
This is the return from interrupt instruction. The Stack is popped and the top of Stack (TOS) is loaded into the program counter. Interrupts must be enabled by setting the global interrupt enable (GIE) bit.

Syntax   RETFIE
Status   –
Cycles   2
Words   1

Example   RETFIE

RETLW
This is a form of the return from sub routine instruction. The literal value 'k' (the value contained within the instruction) is loaded into the W register. The program counter is loaded with the value at the top of the Stack, which is the subroutine address.

Syntax   RETLW   k
Status   –
Cycles   2
Words   1

Example   RETLW   12
          A value of 12 is loaded into the W register. The program counter is loaded from the top of the Stack, and the program continues from where it left off.

RETURN
This is the standard form of the return from subroutine instruction. The Stack is popped and then the top of the Stack (TOS) is loaded into the program counter.

Syntax	RETURN
Status	–
Cycles	2
Words	1

Example   RETURN

RLF

This is the rotate left with carry instruction. The contents of the specified register are rotated one bit to the left through the carry flag. The result is left in the file register if d = 1, or placed in the W register if d = 0.

Syntax	RLF	f,d
Status	C	
Cycles	1	
Words	1	

Example   RLF   18,0

The value in file register 18 is rotated one bit to the left through the carry flag, and the result is placed in the W register. The contents of register 18 are unaffected. If register 18 contained the binary value 10101110, it would still do so after this instruction had been executed, but the W register would contain the value 01010110, and the carry flag would be set.

RRF

This is the rotate right through the carry flag The contents of the specified register are rotated one bit to the right through the carry flag. The result is placed in the W register if d = 0, or back in the file register if d = 1.

Syntax	RRF	f,d
Status	C	
Cycles	1	
Words	1	

Example   RRF   14,1
The value in file register 14 is rotated one bit to the right through the carry flag, and the result is placed in register 14. For instance, if register 14 contained the binary value 10101110 before the instruction was executed, it would contain the value 01010111 afterwards. The carry flag would not be set.

SLEEP
This instruction puts the processor in the sleep mode. This facility is described in detail elsewhere in this publication.

Syntax   SLEEP
Status   TO, PD
Cycles   1
Words   1

Example   SLEEP

SUBLW
The 2s complement method is used to subtract the contents of the W register from the 8-bit literal 'k' (the value contained within the instruction). The result is stored in the W register.

Syntax   SUBLW   k
Status   C, DC, Z
Cycles   1
Words   1

Example   SUBLW   17
The contents of the W register are subtracted from 17, and the result is placed in the W register. If the W register contained 4 prior to this instruction, it would contain 13 afterwards.

SUBWF
The 2s complement method is used to subtract the contents of

the W register from the specified file register. If d = 1 the result is placed in the file register, or if d = 0 it is placed in the W register.

Syntax	SUBWF	f,d
Status	C, DC, Z	
Cycles	1	
Words	1	

Example 1 SUBWF   12, 0

The value in the W register is subtracted from file register 12, and the answer is placed in the W register. If register 12 contains 78, and the W register contains 6, register 12 will still be set at 78 and the W register will be set at 72 after this instruction has executed.

Example 2 SUBWF   12,1

The value in the W register is subtracted from the value in register 12, and the result is placed in register 12. If register 12 contains 78 and the W register contains 6, after the instruction has executed these registers will respectively contain 72 and 6.

SWAPF

The upper and lower nibbles of the specified register are swapped over (i.e. bits 0 to 3 and bits 4 to 7 are swapped). The result is placed in the W register if d = 0, or in the file register if d = 1.

Syntax	SWAPF	f,d
Status	–	
Cycles	1	
Words	1	

Example 1 SWAPF   15,0

The two nibbles in file register 15 are swapped over, and the result is placed in the W register. For

111

instance, if register 15 contained the binary value
00111100, it would still do so after this instruction,
but the W register would contain the binary value
11000011.

Example 2 SWAPF   15,1
The two nibbles in file register 15 are swapped over,
and the result is placed in register 15. If register 15
originally contained the binary value 00111100,
after this instruction it would contain 11000011.

XORLW

The value in the W register is exclusive ORed (XORed) with
the 8-bit literal 'k' (i.e. the value contained within the
instruction). The result is stored in the W register.

Syntax	XORLW k
Status	Z
Cycles	1
Words	1

Example   XORLW   2
The value in the W register is exclusive ORed with
a value of 2 (00000010 in binary). If the W register
contained a value of 00001111, after this instruction the W register would contain 00000010.

XORWF

The contents of the specified register are exclusive ORed with
the contents of the W register. If d = 0 the result is placed in the
W register, but if d = 1 the result is placed in the specified
register.

Syntax	XORFW f,d
Status	Z
Cycles	1
Words	1

Example 1 XORFW   12,0

The contents of register 12 are exclusive ORed with the value in the W register, and the result is stored

in

the W register. If the W register and register 12 respectively contain 11110000 and 01100110, after this instruction the W register would contain 01100000 and register 12 would still contain 01100110.

Example 2 XORFW   12,1

The contents of register 12 are exclusive ORed with the contents of the W register, and the result is stored in register 12. If the W register and register 12 respectively contain 11110000 and 01100110, after this instruction register 12 would contain 01100000 and the W register would still contain 11110000.

The 16C71 also has OPTION and TRIS instructions. However, in order to maintain upward compatibility, the manufacturers recommend that these instructions should not be used with the 16C71. With the 16C54, etc., there is no alternative as these instructions represent the only way of writing data to the OPTION and TRIS registers. Details of the OPTION and TRIS instructions are therefore provided here.

OPTION
Copies the contents of the W register to the OPTION register.

Syntax   OPTION
Status   –
Cycles   1
Words   1

Example   OPTION
Copies the value in the W register to the OPTION register. Obviously the appropriate value must be loaded into the W register before this instruction is issued.

TRIS

Copies the contents of the W register to the specified TRIS register.

Syntax	TRIS	f
Status	–	
Cycles	1	
Words	1	

Example   TRIS   5

Copies the value in the W register to TRIS register 5. TRIS registers 5, 6, and 7 correspond to TRISA, TRISB, and TRISC respectively. Obviously the appropriate value must be loaded in the W register before this instruction is issued.

The following table lists the 16C71 instruction set, and is useful as a memory aid when you start writing PIC software.

Mnemonic	Basic Function	Cycles
ADDLW	Add k to W	1
ADDWF	Add W to f	1
ANDLW	Bitwise AND W with k	1
ANDWF	Bitwise AND W with f	1
BCF	Bit clear f	1
BSF	Bit set f	1
BTFSC	Bit test – skip if clear	1 or 2
BTFSS	Bit test – skip if set	1 or 2
CALL	Call subroutine	2
CLRF	Clear f	1
CLRW	Clear W	1
CLRWDT	Clear watchdog timer	1
COMF	Complement f	1
DECF	Decrement f	1
DECFSZ	Decrement f and skip if 0	1 or 2
GOTO	Unconditional branch	2
INCF	Increment f	1
INCFSZ	Increment f and skip if 0	1 or 2
IORLW	Bitwise OR k with W	1

IORWF	Bitwise OR W with f	1
MOVLW	Move k to W	1
MOVF	Move f	1
MOVWF	Move W to f	1
NOP	No operation	1
OPTION	Load option register	1
RETFIE	Return from interrupt	2
RETLW	Return, k to W	2
RETURN	Return from subroutine	2
RLF	Rotate left through carry	1
RRF	Rotate right through carry	1
SLEEP	Enter sleep mode	1
SUBLW	Subtract W from k	1
SUBWF	Subtract W from f	1
SWAPF	Swap f	1
TRIS	Load TRIS register	1
XORLW	Bitwise XOR k with W	1
XORWF	XOR W with f	1

The following lists place the instructions into three categories, which might make it easier to find a mnemonic or instruction when you initially start writing PIC software.

Operations on File Register Bytes

ADDWF	Add W to f
ANDWF	Bitwise AND W with f
CLRF	Clear f
CLRW	Clear W
COMF	Complement f
DEC	Decrement f
DECFSZ	Decrement f, skip if zero
INCF	Increment f
INCFSZ	Increment f, skip if zero
IORWF	Bitwise OR W with f
MOVF	Move f
MOVWF	Move contents of W to f
RLF	Rotate left through carry
RRF	Rotate right through carry
SUBWF	Subtract W from f

| SWAPF | Swap W with f |
| XORWF | Bitwise exclusive OR W with f |

Operations on File Register Bits
BCF	Bit clear f
BSF	Bit set f
BTFSC	Bit test f and skip if clear
BTFSS	Bit test f and skip if set

Operations, Literal and Control
ADDLW	Add literal to W
ANDLW	Bitwise AND literal and W
CALL	Call subroutine
CLRWDT	Clear watchdog timer
GOTO	Go to instruction address
IORLW	Bitwise OR literal with W
MOVLW	Move literal to W
NOP	No operation
RETFIE	Return from interrupt
RETLW	Return and put literal in W
SLEEP	Go into SLEEP (standby) mode
SUBLW	Subtract literal from W
XORLW	Exclusive OR literal with W

Points to Remember

When writing assembly language programs use mnemonics for the instructions. The assembler converts these into their corresponding binary values.

Assembly language programs contain four fields (labels, mnemonics for instructions, operands, and comments).

You do not have to bother about keeping track of instruction addresses. You just assign labels to any points in the program, and the assembler assigns suitable addresses to them. This makes it easy to program loops and subroutines.

With many PIC instructions the result of an operation can be stored in the W register ($d = 0$) or in the appropriate file register ($d = 1$).

There are only about three dozen PIC instructions and they are mostly quite simple, so try to learn them all before you get into serious PIC programming.

The 16C5* series processors need the OPTION and TRIS instructions to load the OPTION and TRIS registers, but the later processors such as the 16C71 can access them using other instructions.

Chapter 5

GETTING IT TOGETHER

In the previous chapters various aspects of PIC microcontrollers have been covered, and in this chapter we will look at how these aspects are combined to produce some simple PIC based devices. The hardware and software have been kept very simple as their purpose is to provide an introduction to practical PIC design, rather than to act as genuinely useful projects. When first undertaking PIC design work it is definitely a good idea to keep things simple, and work on the premise that it is 'better to learn to walk before you try to run'.

Four Aspect Signal

The first design example is a simple signal for a model train-set. Rather than a simple three-aspect (red – amber – green) signal, this one is based on the 'real thing' used on the suburban railway which passes near to where I live. The signals on this railway use four-aspect signals which go to red as a train passes, to amber and amber when the train has moved a certain distance from the signal, then to single amber when it has moved further along the line, and finally back to green when the train has moved still further along the line. This basic design does not respond to the model train, but simply cycles the signal through its four states.

When designing a PIC system you must start with the hardware, because the software has to be designed to suit the hardware set-up selected. In this case we simply need to drive four LEDs from outputs of the processor. No other inputs or outputs are needed, so the most simple of PIC devices can handle the task. We will therefore base the unit on a 16C54, which has one 8-bit port (Port B) and one 4-bit type (Port A). In this case we only need four outputs, and either port could be used. It really does not matter which port is used, and my selection of RB0 to RB3 (i.e. the lower nibble of Port B) is a purely arbitrary one.

The other main decision to make is the type of clock oscillator to be used, and the clock frequency. At first sight this might look like a prime candidate for a very low clock frequency, since we require a gap of several seconds from one change in the signal to the next. Using a very low clock frequency would enable the software to be very simple indeed, with no delay loops. In practice there would be a drawback to using a very low clock frequency, which is simply that the signal would be non-operational for some time after switch-on while the processor performed the initial instructions to set up Port B. It would therefore be better to use a higher clock frequency and delay loops to hold the signal at each state for the required length of time. There is no need to use a clock frequency of more than a few hertz, as this is sufficient to keep the initial setting up period suitably short. A higher clock frequency would complicate matters by requiring relatively long and complex program loops to hold the signal at each state for an adequate period. In an undemanding application such as this a C-R clock oscillator is perfectly adequate.

It did not take too long to arrive at the circuit of Figure 5.1. A PIC port can source a high enough current to drive LEDs, but the usual current limiting resistors (R2 to R5) are needed to protect the port outputs from excessive loading. The built-in reset circuit can be used, and MCLR (pin 4) is therefore connected to the +5 volt supply rail. The RTCC pin is not used in this application, but it must not be left 'floating'. It is therefore tied to the +5 volt supply rail as well.

R1 and C2 are the timing components in the C-R clock oscillator. The clock circuit is a very simple relaxation oscillator which uses the arrangement shown in Figure 5.2. The capacitor (C2) charges by way of R1 until the charge potential is high enough to send the output of the trigger circuit high. The N channel MOSFET then switches on and discharges C2 until the charge voltage is low enough to set the output of the trigger circuit low again. C2 then starts to charge once more, and the circuit oscillates indefinitely in this manner, producing a sawtooth waveform across C2 and a roughly squarewave output signal from the trigger circuit. It is the squarewave that is used as the clock signal for the microcontroller. Operation of this type of oscillator relies on the hysteresis of the trigger circuit. In other words, its reluctance to change back to its previous state once it has been triggered. The input voltage

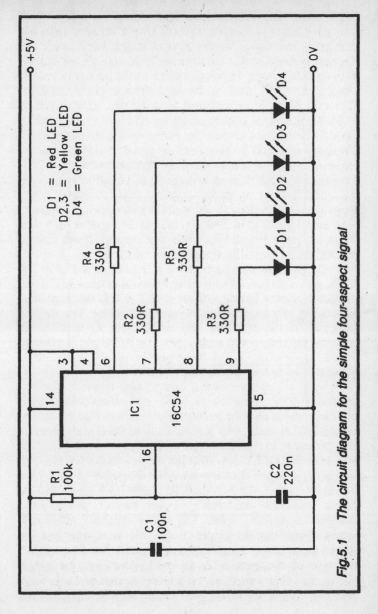

Fig.5.1 The circuit diagram for the simple four-aspect signal

121

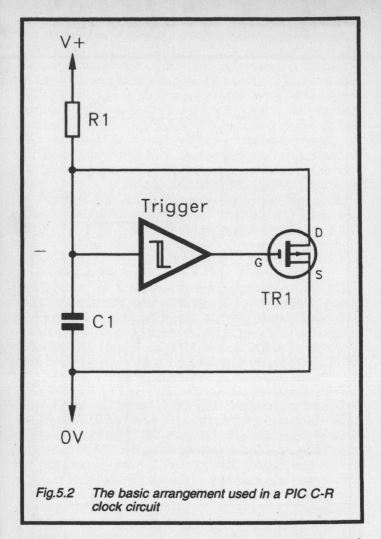

Fig.5.2   The basic arrangement used in a PIC C-R clock circuit

which causes the output to trigger to the high state is much higher than the one which causes it to revert to the low state.

This type of oscillator is a good choice for a general purpose but inexact clock oscillator. It can operate over a very wide frequency range of well under one hertz to a maximum of a few megahertz. The drawback is that a circuit of this type lacks frequency accuracy and stability. Changes in temperature can affect the values of the timing components, and produce significant frequency drift. The tolerance of these components also limits the accuracy with which the clock frequency can be set. The main problem is the trigger circuit though. The operating frequency is dependent on the two trigger voltages, and these vary considerably from one device to another. Also, as a percentage of the supply voltage, they change with fluctuations in the supply voltage. This type of clock circuit is therefore unsuitable where the clock frequency must be set accurately, and (or) it must be highly stable.

Practical tests suggest that with the timing resistance at around 100k, a low clock frequency, and a 5 volt supply, the clock frequency is approximately equal to:

$$1/(C1 \times R1)$$

Calculating the output frequency is easier if the values of the timing components are expressed in megohms and microfarads rather than ohms and farads. The values used in the circuit of Figure 5.1 (100k and 220n) produce an approximate clock frequency of 60Hz, and the measured output frequency from the clock output pin was 14.8Hz. The clock output signal is at one-quarter of the clock frequency though, and 14.8Hz is therefore quite close to the expected figure of 15Hz. Using the software I eventually devised for this project, it takes a little under two minutes for the circuit to go through one complete cycle of the signal lights, but the speed of the circuit is easily changed by altering the value of C2. For example, a value of 120n would almost double the clock frequency, and reduce the time for one complete cycle of the lights to about one minute . In some cases you may not be able to select the final clock frequency until the software has been completed, but you should at least be able to get reasonably close with your initial estimate.

The following table should prove helpful when selecting values for timing components in the clock oscillator. It simply gives suggested values for a range of clock frequencies.

Frequency	C	R
1Hz	10μ	100k
2Hz	4μ7	100k
5Hz	2μ2	110k
10Hz	1μ	100k
20Hz	470n	100k
50Hz	150n	120k
100Hz	68n	100k
200Hz	33n	82k
500Hz	15n	47k
1kHz	47n	12k
2kHz	100n	10k
5kHz	22n	22k
10kHz	4n7	12k
20kHz	2n2	15k
50kHz	2n2	8k2
100kHz	2n2	3k9
200kHz	1n	3k9
500kHz	470p	3k3
1MHz	150p	4k7
2MHz	82p	4k3
4MHz	33p	3k9

These values take into account the input capacitance of the processor chip itself, and loading by the trigger circuit. Thus, although there may seem to be some discrepancies, they are actually correct. Note that these values will only give something close to the specified frequencies, and that errors of 10 per cent or more can occur even if close tolerance components are used. Operation at frequencies of more than 4MHz using a C-R oscillator is not recommended, although it is possible with the faster chips if you are prepared to 'turn a blind eye' to the manufacturer's recommendations.

Software
No doubt there are endless ways of obtaining the desired action from this circuit, and the listing shown here is just one possibility.

```
;***************************************************
;Basic Signal Program
;***************************************************
;
;
            MOVLW    00
            TRIS     06        ;Sets Port B bits 0 to 3 as outputs
LOOP        MOVLW    01
            MOVWF    06        ;Sets signal to green
            BCF      03,2      ;Resets zero flag
            MOVLW    7F        ;Number of loops
            MOVWF    0C
DELAY1      DECFSZ   0C,1
            GOTO     DELAY1    ;Sets green signal time
            MOVLW    08
            MOVWF    06        ;Sets signal to red
            BCF      03,2      ;Resets zero flag
            MOVLW    50        ;Number of loops
            MOVWF    0C
DELAY2      DECFSZ   0C,1
            GOTO     DELAY2    ;Sets red signal time
            MOVLW    06
            MOVWF    06        ;Sets signal to twin amber
            BCF      03,2      ;Resets zero flag
            MOVLW    50
            MOVWF    0C
DELAY3      DECFSZ   0C,1
            GOTO     DELAY3
            MOVLW    02
            MOVWF    06        ;Sets signal to amber
            BCF      03,2      ;Resets zero flag
            MOVLW    50        ;Number of loops
            MOVWF    0C
DELAY4      DECFSZ   0C1,
            GOTO     DELAY4
            GOTO     LOOP
            END
```

It has to be pointed out that different assemblers do things in slightly different ways, and you therefore need to read the 'fine print' to determine the exact format that your assembler requires. Some require a 'tab' character or several spaces between fields, while others will settle for a single space character. Some need a colon (:) at the end of the labels in the labels field (to ensure that labels are not confused with mnemonics), while others do not. The need for a semicolon (;) character at the beginning of comments seems to be needed with all assemblers. As you will see from this listing, the use of comments is not restricted to added notes at the end of instructions. The assembler ignores anything that follows a semicolon and is on the same line. You can therefore add as many lines of notes as you like at the beginning of a listing provided each one starts with a semicolon. This facility can be used to give a listing, a title, provide basic details of the hardware configuration, or to include any information that might be useful to you if you return to the program at some later date. This information can also be useful to anyone who makes use of your programs.

The listings in this chapter are in a form that is suitable for the 'MPALC' or 'MPASM' assemblers produced by Microchip Technologies Incorporated (the PIC chip manufacturers). Other assemblers might need the listing to be 'fine tuned' in order to get it to assemble correctly. Assemblers usually give you the option of using decimal numbers, but use hexadecimal by default. The programs in this chapter all use hexadecimal numbers, and there is probably no point in using decimal even if it is available as an option. Hexadecimal is much more convenient for this sort of low-level programming.

The first step is to set up RB0 to RB3 as outputs, and this is the purpose of the first two lines of the program. The first line moves a value of zero into the W register, and the second line loads this into TRISB. This actually sets all eight lines of Port B as outputs, but it does not matter whether RA4 to RA7 are inputs or outputs. The next two lines write a value of 1 to Port B, which sets RB0 high and switches on D4 (the green LED). The program must then loop a number of times in order to hold the signal at green for a suitable period. First the zero flag in the status register must be reset, as it is this bit being set that brings the loop to an end. Before using a status bit you should always ensure that it is at the appropriate starting state by setting it at that state. If you just assume that it is at the correct state it is reasonable to expect a fair proportion of your programs to fail! A value of 7F is then moved into the W register, and from here it is copied to register 0C, which is used as the counter. The next two lines form the actual loop, and a DECFSZ instruction is used to decrement register 0C. A GOTO instruction keeps looping the program back to this instruction, but only until the value in register 0C reaches zero. The zero flag in the status register is then set, and the DECFSZ instruction jumps over the GOTO instruction.

This breaks the program out of the loop, but it then goes into a virtually identical routine that sets the signal to red and provides another delay. This is followed by similar routines that set the signal to amber and amber, and then single amber, again with a delay being provided in each routine. The number of loops used while the signal is at red, amber – amber, and amber is lower than number used while it is green. This has been done to set the signal to green for longer than it is set to the other colours, but there is clearly no difficulty in altering the four delay times to suit individual requirements. It is just a matter of changing the number of loops used in the routine for each signal. This sort of versatility is one of the main attractions of using microcontrollers. A basic design can be 'fine tuned' to suit individual requirements by changing the software, with changes in the hardware often being unnecessary.

Once the signal has been at amber for the appropriate time the program loops back to almost the beginning, and goes through the sequence once again. There is obviously no point in performing the first two instructions on each loop of the program, as it is only necessary to set up Port B once. The 'END' instruction does not actually produce any code for the processor, and this simply indicates to the assembler that it has reached the end of the program listing.

Refinements

With a simple program such as this there is no difficulty in keeping track of the functions assigned to the general purpose file registers, since only one of them is actually utilized (file 0C). Life obviously gets more difficult when you start to write programs that use a few dozen of these registers. It would obviously be more convenient if the registers could be referred

127

to by a meaningful name, and there would also be less risk of errors occurring when writing the code. It would also be easier if the status register and its flags could simply be referred to by name. Some assemblers do actually permit the status register and the flags to be specified by name rather than by register and bit numbers, but this is by no means a universal feature.

Any PIC assembler should support symbols, and these enable registers, etc., to be specified using a name rather than a number. It is really just a matter of adding a list at the beginning of each program, declaring the symbols and the values each one represents. This is done using the EQU (equals) command. In the signal program register 0C is used as a counter, and it could therefore be called something like 'COUNTER' or 'CNTR'. It is up to the programmer to select suitable names, but note that there might be a restriction on the number of characters allowed, and some characters may not be permissible. Symbols usually have to start with a letter of the alphabet rather than a number. The assembler may differentiate between upper and lower case letters, or there may be the option to enable you to switch case sensitivity on and off. Once again, it is a matter of going through the manual and reading the 'fine print'. It is advisable to keep symbols precise and to the point even if long names are permitted.

This version of the signal program shows how symbols can be used. The symbol called 'CNTR' is assigned to a value of 0C, 'STATUS' is assigned a value of '03', and Z is assigned a value of 2. These symbols can then be used in the program instead of the values they represent (e.g. BCF STATUS,Z instead of BCF 03,2). The program 'blown' into the PIC chip is exactly the same for both versions of the program. Symbols make it easier for the programmer to write programs and to avoid errors, but have no affect on the final program. Many programmers have a standard set of symbols that they use at the start of every program. Obviously some customising will normally be required in order to make the standard set of symbols suit each new program, but some customising is usually a lot quicker than 'starting from scratch' each time you write a program.

```
;***************************************************
;Signal Program Using Symbols
;***************************************************
;
CNTR      EQU       OC          ;Sets counter as file 0C
STATUS    EQU       03
Z         EQU       2
          MOVLW     00
          TRIS      06          ;Sets Port B bits 0 to 3 as outputs
LOOP      MOVLW     01
          MOVWF     06          ;Sets signal to green
          BCF       STATUS,Z    ;Resets zero flag
          MOVLW     7F          ;Number of loops
          MOVWF     CNTR
DELAY1    DECFSZ    CNTR,1
          GOTO      DELAY1      ;Sets green signal time
          MOVLW     08
          MOVWF     06          ;Sets signal to red
          BCF       STATUS,Z    ;Resets zero flag
          MOVLW     50          ;Number of loops
          MOVWF     CNTR
DELAY2    DECFSZ    CNTR,1
          GOTO      DELAY2      ;Sets red signal time
          MOVLW     06
          MOVWF     06          ;Sets signal to twin amber
          BCF       STATUS,Z    ;Resets zero flag
          MOVLW     50          ;Number of loops
          MOVWF     CNTR
DELAY3    DECFSZ    CNTR,1
          GOTO      DELAY3      ;Sets twin amber signal time
          MOVLW     02
          MOVWF     06          ;Sets signal to amber
          BCF       STATUS,Z    ;Resets zero flag
          MOVLW     50          ;Number of loops
          MOVWF     CNTR
DELAY4    DECFSZ    CNTR,1
          GOTO      DELAY4
          GOTO      LOOP
          END
```

Chip Programming

The exact procedure for 'blowing' the program into the PIC processor depends on the particular programming or development system that you are using. Typically you would first run the assembler, selecting the source file, processor type, output file format, etc., before getting it to produce a file containing the object code for the programmer. When you are developing your own programs you will probably wish to run some sort of simulator before 'blowing' the program into the chip. If you are simply copying a tried and tested program this stage is not necessary, provided you are confident that your copy of the program is accurate. Before 'blowing' a program into a one-time programmable chip you obviously need to be reasonably sure that the program is correct, since even the most simple of errors will result in a programmed chip that is completely useless.

Having successfully produced the object code for the chip it is then a matter of running the software for the programmer, and then selecting the appropriate options for your project. For example, you must select whether or not you require the code protection flag to be set, and where appropriate you must also select the appropriate clock type. Of course, with many of the one-time programmable chips you do not have to select the clock type as the chip will only support one type. When you are sure that everything is set up correctly, the program is 'blown' into the chip. However, if the processor is a type which can be re-programmed you should always check that it has been properly erased before re-programming it. Any programming system should have a facility to check that the device has been properly erased. Having 'blown' the program into the chip the contents are usually verified by the programming software, but you may have to invoke this routine manually. If the program in the chip does not match the object code there is almost certainly a hardware fault, and the most likely cause of the problem is that the PIC processor itself is faulty.

If you try the simple signal project it can easily be built on a solderless breadboard, but as PIC processors are static-sensitive remember to observe the usual handling precautions. Presumably the program would be 'blown' into a re-programmable chip, and these are not exactly cheap. This makes it all the more important to observe the normal anti-static handling precautions. When experimenting with PIC processors I would certainly recommend using an earthed mat on the workbench, and it is also a good idea to wear an earthed wrist-band so that you are not in any danger of 'zapping' a PIC chip every time you handle one.

Automatic Signal

We will now take our model train signal example a stage further, and produce an automatic version which is operated by the train via reed or micro-switches on the track. This is much the same as the example system that was described in Chapter 1, but with the same form of four-aspect signalling that is used in the simple signal described in the previous section of this chapter. In fact the output side of the signal can be left unchanged, and it is just a matter of monitoring the switches by way of four inputs on the processor. RB4 to RB7 and RA0 to RA3 are available for this purpose, and we will keep things straightforward by using separate ports for the input and output lines. Therefore, RA0 to RA3 are used to monitor the sensor switches, and it does not really matter which input monitors which switch, since the software can be written to suit any set-up. We will use the arrangement outlined in Figure 5.3.

When writing software for an application such as this it is more than a little helpful if the basic action of the system is defined first. In fact it is probably easier to start with a simple list that relates input and output states to their corresponding 'real world' events. All that is needed is a simple list of the type that follows.

Red signal	Write 8 to Port B
Amber ×2 signal	Write 6 to Port B
Amber signal	Write 2 to Port B
Green signal	Write 1 to Port B
Switch 1 activated	Port A bit 0 set
Switch 2 activated	Port A bit 1 set
Switch 3 activated	Port A bit 2 set
Switch 4 activated	Port A bit 3 set

In order to produce a single amber signal either 2 or 4 can be written to Port B, since switching on either of the yellow

131

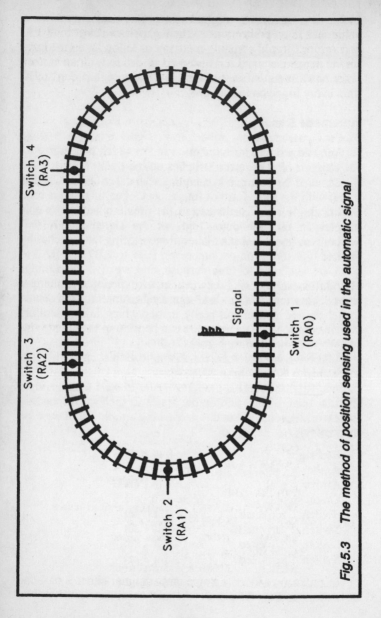

Fig.5.3 The method of position sensing used in the automatic signal

LEDs will provide the desired result. The decision to use a value of 2 is an arbitrary one. Having written down the basic port information in a way that is easy to follow, keep it handy for reference purposes, and proceed to produce either a flow chart or a list to define the steps that the program must take. This is my suggested list of program steps.

1. Set Port B as outputs (Port A defaults to inputs).
2. Set signal at green.
3. Read Port A and store result.
4. Check if bit 0 of result is high, set signal to red if it is.
5. Check if bit 1 of result is high, set signal to amber ×2 if it is.
6. Check if bit 2 of result is high, set signal to amber if it is.
7. Check if bit 3 of result is high, set signal to green if it is.
8. Loop to line 3 and read Port A, etc. again.
9. End.

This list converts quite easily into an actual program, and this is the listing for the automatic signal program.

```
;************************************************
;Automatic Model Train Signal Program
;Red on RB3, amber on RB1/2, green on RB0
;S1 to S4 on RA0 to RA3 respectively
;************************************************
;
;
INPUT     EQU     05
OUTPUT    EQU     06
STORE     EQU     0C
          MOVLW   00
          TRIS    6           ;Port B as outputs
          MOVLW   01
          MOVWF   OUTPUT      ;Set signal to green initially
LOOP      MOVF    INPUT,W     ;Read Port A
          MOVWF   STORE       ;Store reading
          MOVLW   08
          BTFSC   STORE,0     ;If RA0 high
          MOVWF   OUTPUT      ;Set signal to red
          MOVLW   06
```

133

```
BTFSC      STORE,1     ;If RA1 high
MOVWF      OUTPUT      ;Set signal to twin amber
MOVLW      02
BTFSC      STORE,2     ;If RA2 high
MOVWF      OUTPUT      ;Set signal to amber
MOVLW      01
BTFSC      STORE,3     ;If RA3 high
MOVWF      OUTPUT      ;Set signal to green
GOTO       LOOP
END
```

The first three lines of the program define symbols for the input port (INPUT), the output port (OUTPUT), and the register used to store the values read from Port A (STORE). It would be possible to use further symbols, such as a value of 01 for GREEN and 08 for RED, but with such a simple program this would not really be worthwhile. The program continues by setting Port B as an output port, but there is no need to set Port A as an input port as this is the default condition. The next two lines of the program set the signal to its initial state of green. After this initial setting up the program enters the main loop section, and this starts with Port A being read and the returned value is then transferred to STORE (file register 0C).

In order to obtain the desired action the program must test bits 0 to 3 of STORE, one-by-one, and set the signal to the appropriate state if one of these bits is set. This requires a conditional instruction that acts on the state of a particular bit in the specified file. The 16C54 instruction set has only one instruction which fits our requirements, and this is BTFSC. This instruction carries on to the next instruction if the bit that is tested is set to one, but it skips the next instruction if it is set to zero. The first BTFSC instruction tests to see if bit 0 (RA0) is set to one. If it is, S1 has been activated and the signal must be set to red. This is accomplished by the next instruction, but if bit 0 is zero, this instruction is skipped. A further three pairs of instructions test bits 1 to 3 and provide the appropriate action if one of these bits is set to one. In every case, setting the signal to the correct state must be accomplished in a single instruction, as only one instruction can be skipped over if a bit is not set to one. The appropriate value is therefore moved into the W register before each bit is tested. If the bit is set to one, it then only takes a single instruction to transfer the value from the W register to Port B.

Once the full set of 4-bit tests have been completed the program is looped back to the point where Port A is read, and this whole process repeats indefinitely. The sensor switches may only close very briefly as the model train passes, and a reasonably high clock frequency is therefore needed in order to ensure that the circuit always responds properly. The circuit could be made to loop every one or two microseconds by using a very high clock frequency, but this is not necessary as the mechanical characteristics of the switches mean that they must close for at least a few milliseconds. A clock frequency of about 1MHz is therefore more than adequate to ensure that the circuit operates reliably. Each time a switch is activated, the unit will set the signal to the appropriate state over and over again. For as long as the sensor switch is closed, the signal will be set to the appropriate state. Repeated looping of this type is not acceptable in some applications, but it is of no consequence in this case. Setting the signal to its existing state simply has no effect, and will not cause a malfunction.

The circuit diagram for the automatic signal appears in Figure 5.4. The output side of the circuit is identical to the basic signal circuit described previously. On the input side there is a pull-down resistor for each input, plus a sensor switch that pulls the input high when it is activated. The values of R5 and C2 set the clock frequency at about 4MHz, but the circuit should work equally well using a much lower clock frequency. This is obviously another circuit that could be tested quite easily by building it on a solderless breadboard. S1 to S4 could simply be pushbutton switches in the test circuit.

Subroutines

With this simple application it is possible to avoid the use of subroutines because the signal can be set to the required state in a single instruction. With many applications a single instruction will not be adequate, and a subroutine then becomes the only way of handling things. Subroutines are very easy to use, and it is just a matter of using the CALL instruction to enter the subroutine, and some form of RETURN instruction to jump

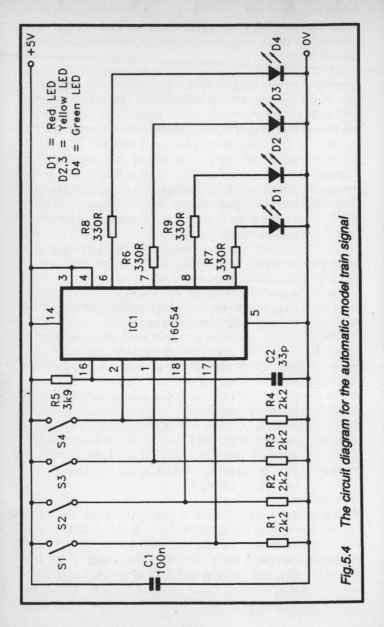

D1 = Red LED
D2,3 = Yellow LED
D4 = Green LED

Fig.5.4   The circuit diagram for the automatic model train signal

136

back into the main program once the routine has been completed. This listing provides the automatic signal function using subroutines.

```
;************************************************
;AUTOMATIC TRAIN SIGNAL PROGRAM USING
SUBROUTINES
;************************************************
;
INPUT    EQU      05
OUTPUT   EQU      06
STORE    EQU      0C
         MOVLW    00
         TRIS     6            ;Port B as outputs
         MOVLW    01
         MOVWF    OUTPUT       ;Set signal to green initially
LOOP     MOVF     INPUT,W      ;Read Port A
         MOVWF    STORE        ;Store reading
         BTFSC    STORE,0      ;If RA0 high
         CALL     RED          ;Call red routine
         BTFSC    STORE,1      ;If RA1 high
         CALL     AMBR2        ;Call twin amber routine
         BTFSC    STORE,2      ;If RA2 high
         CALL     AMBER        ;Call amber routine
         BTFSC    STORE,3      ;If RA3 high
         CALL     GREEN        ;Call green routine
         GOTO     LOOP
RED      MOVLW    08           ;Set signal to red
         MOVWF    OUTPUT
         RETLW    00
AMBR2    MOVLW    06           ;Set signal to twin amber
         MOVWF    OUTPUT
         RETLW    00
AMBER    MOVLW    02           ;Set signal to amber
         MOVWF    OUTPUT
         RETLW    00
GREEN    MOVLW    01           ;Set signal to green
         MOVWF    OUTPUT
         RETLW    00
         END
```

The initial part of the program is exactly the same as in the original version, with the symbols being defined, Port B being set as an output port, and the signal being set to green. The decision making process is similar to that in the original program, but the appropriate value is not loaded into the W register before the bit testing is carried out. Also, if a bit is set to one, the program proceeds to the next instruction where a suitable subroutine is CALLed. The subroutines are defined at the end of the program.

Using subroutines is very simple with the 16C54 since you do not have to bother about the Stack. The processor automatically stores the appropriate address on the Stack, and loads it into the program counter at the end of the routine. In order to enter a subroutine you simply use a CALL instruction with a label indicating the start address of the routine (such as 'GREEN' or 'AMBER' in this program). A RETURN instruction at the end of the routine takes things back to the instruction that follows the one which CALLed the subroutine. The 16C54 does not have a straightforward RETURN instruction, but it does have RETLW. This places the literal number (i.e. the number specified within the instruction) in the W register when the program returns from the subroutine. This loading of the W register is of no help in the current application, and a 'dummy' value of zero is therefore used in each RETLW instruction.

The label used when calling a subroutine represents an instruction address, not a data register address. There is no risk of getting the two confused since you do not need to deal with instruction addresses in number form. You simply assign a label to a subroutine, and the assembler allocates a suitable instruction address to that label. Unless you look at the assembled code to find out, you never know what address is assigned to each label, and do not need to know.

Subroutines are an important part of any programming, and it is quite normal for a program to consist of a main loop which calls up numerous subroutines. The subroutines will normally be more complex than the ones used in this program, but the general format of this program is one that is applicable to many practical applications. An advantage of this approach is that it is easy to modify the software to support new features. In most cases a small addition to the main loop plus an extra subroutine will be sufficient to add the new feature.

Looking Up

On the face of it there is no way that the ROM can be used to store data, as it is strictly for storing instructions. Closer examination of the instruction set reveals that there are instructions that load literal values (values contained within the instructions) into the W register. Data can therefore be stored in these instructions, and called up when required. This is fine for the odd byte of data here and there, but how can a block of ROM be used to store numerous bytes of data? Practical applications often require blocks of data for use as lookup tables. As a simple but practical example, suppose that we require a circuit that takes a 4-bit binary code and displays its decimal equivalent via a 7-segment LED display. In other words, a basic binary coded decimal decoder for a 7-segment display.

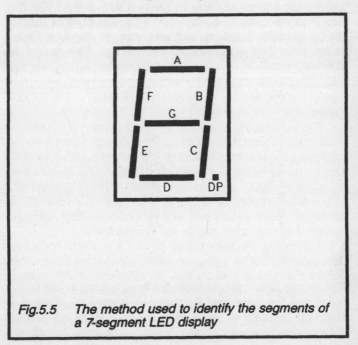

Fig.5.5   The method used to identify the segments of a 7-segment LED display

The segments of a 7-segment display are identified by the letters of the alphabet from 'A' to 'G', as shown in Figure 5.5. All real-world displays seem to have an eighth segment in the form of the decimal point ('DP') LED, but this is of no importance in the present context. We simply require a circuit that will take the 4-bit binary input signal and convert it to a 7-bit code that will produce the appropriate decimal numbers on the display. There are two types of LED display, which are the common cathode and common anode varieties. We will use the common cathode type, which require a high (logic 1) output level to switch on a segment.

There are probably several ways of using a PIC processor to handle this form of decoding, but the most common approach is to use a lookup table. This table contains the values that must be sent to the output port in order to produce each of the numbers from 0 to 9. We will assume here that the segments from A to G are driven from RB0 to RB6 of the PIC processor, and that the 4-bit input codes are read via RA0 to RA3. The first task is to work out the binary code needed to produce each of the ten possible numbers, and then convert the 7-bit binary codes into their hexadecimal equivalents. This gives the following result.

Number	Hex Value
0	3F
1	06
2	5B
3	4F
4	66
5	6D
6	7D
7	07
8	7F
9	6F

The lookup table contains these ten hexadecimal values in this order, and the value read from Port A is used as an offset to select the appropriate value. With the PIC processors you are not exactly 'spoilt for choice' when it comes to branch and jump instructions, and in order to implement a lookup table it is necessary to directly control the program counter at file register 02. This 7-segment decoder program illustrates how this is done.

```
;************************************************
;Binary to 7-segment display decoder program
;************************************************
;
        CLRW
        TRIS      06          ;Set B as outputs, A as inputs
START   MOVF      05,W        ;Load W from Port A
        CALL      TABLE       ;Load W from lookup table
        MOVWF     06          ;Output data to Port B
        GOTO      START       ;End of loop
TABLE   ADDWF     02,1        ;Lookup table
        RETLW     3F          ;0
        RETLW     06          ;1
        RETLW     5B          ;2
        RETLW     4F          ;3
        RETLW     66          ;4
        RETLW     6D          ;5
        RETLW     7D          ;6
        RETLW     07          ;7
        RETLW     7F          ;8
        RETLW     6F          ;9
        END
```

The first two instructions simply set Port B as an output port. Port A requires no setting up as it defaults to an input port. The next four lines form a loop which reads Port A, gets the corresponding value from the lookup table, and then outputs this value to Port B. The lookup table is contained in a subroutine called 'TABLE', and this consists of an ADDWF instruction followed by ten RETLW instructions. The ADDWF instruction takes the value in file register 05 (the Port B file register) and adds it to the program counter (file register 02). If the value read from Port A is zero, the program counter is not incremented, and the next instruction is performed in the usual way. This is a RETLW instruction, which returns the program

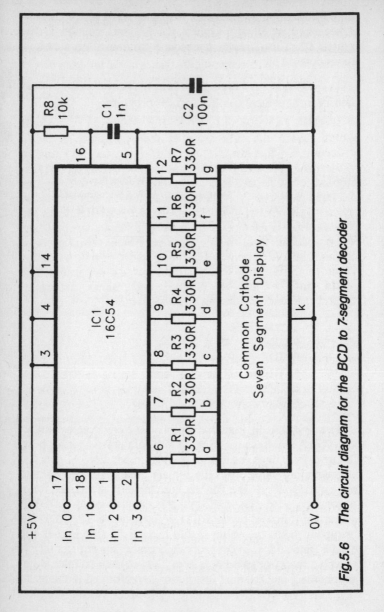

Fig.5.6   The circuit diagram for the BCD to 7-segment decoder

from the subroutine and places a value of 3F in the W register. This is the hexadecimal code required to produce '0' on the display. If the value returned from Port A is 1, the program counter would be incremented by one, and the program would jump to the second RETLW instruction. This instruction returns the program from the subroutine and places a value of 06 in the W register (the value added to produce '1' on the display).

It should be apparent that the value read from Port A will always branch the subroutine to the appropriate RETLW instruction, so that the correct value is loaded into the W register and written to Port B. If you would like to try out this program, it can be used in conjunction with the circuit diagram of Figure 5.6. The 7-segment display can be any common-cathode type, but a high brightness display is preferable as the drive current for each segment is not very high. The program does not include error trapping to handle input values of more than nine, but out of range input values do not seem to cause the system to crash. However, in a 'real' project things like this should not be left to chance, and where necessary comprehensive error trapping must be included.

A/D Conversion

As pointed out in Chapter 4, the 16C71 has a built-in four channel analogue to digital converter which enables it to function in a variety of control and measurement applications with a minimal amount of additional hardware. The converter is quite easy to use, but it is a good idea to try out one or two simple test circuits before trying to do anything too clever with this device. This simple program, together with the circuit of Figure 5.7, provides a basic analogue to digital converter function. The input signal is provided by VR1, and the outputs of the converter are monitored by eight LEDs. D1 is driven by the least significant bit, running through to D8 which is driven by the most significant bit. By adjusting VR1 is should be possible to obtain any 8-bit binary pattern on the LEDs, from all the LEDs switched off with the wiper of VR1 at the 0 volt end of the track, to all LEDs switched on with the wiper at the +5 volt end.

143

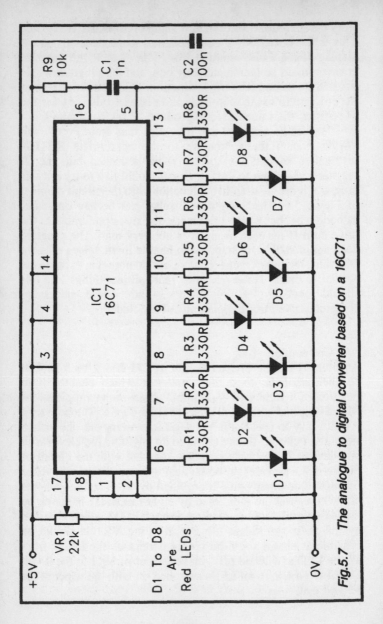

Fig.5.7 The analogue to digital converter based on a 16C71

```
;*************************************************
;A/D Converter program
;*************************************************
;
STATUS    EQU       03
BDIR      EQU       06
ADCON     EQU       08
PORTB     EQU       06
ADRES     EQU       09
          BSF       STATUS,5    ;Select page 1
          CLRW
          MOVWF     BDIR        ;Sets Port B as outputs
          CLRF      ADCON       ;Sets RA0-3 as A/D inputs
          BCF       STATUS,5    ;Select page 0
          MOVLW     0xC1
          MOVWF     ADCON       ;Select Ch0/Int clock
LOOP      BSF       ADCON,2     ;Start conversion
          NOP                   ;Wait
          MOVF      ADRES,0     ;Place conversion in W
          MOVWF     PORTB       ;Output conversion to Port B
          GOTO      LOOP        ;Loop indefinitely
          END
```

The first five lines of the program assign values to labels, and then the first line of code selects page 1 of the data map. Remember that, unlike the 16C54, the 16C71 has two pages of registers, with the required page being selected via bit 5 of the Status register. This is set to 0 if page 0 is required, and to 1 if page 1 is needed. The manufacturer's data has page 0 mapped from 00 to 7F, and page 1 from 80 to FF, but this is perhaps a bit misleading. You can not read from and write to the page 1 registers at addresses from 80 to FF. Instead, bit 5 of the Status register is set to 1, and the page 1 registers are accessed via addresses from 00 to 7F. They occupy the same part of the data map as the page 0 registers, and you use bit 5 of the Status register to switch from one to the other. In this case we are selecting page 1 so that the data direction register for Port B (TRISB) can be cleared, which sets all the Port B lines as outputs. The 16C71 does have the TRIS instruction, but the manufacturer's data recommends that in order to maintain 'upward compatibility' it should not be used. Instead, page 1 is selected, and TRISB is accessed at address 06.

A CLRF instruction then sets all bits of the ADCON1 register to zero, and this sets all four lines of Port A as inputs. In this case we only require RA0 as an analogue input, and will not be using the other lines of Port A at all. Therefore, the value written to ADCON1 is not of great significance, since any value will set RA0 as an analogue input!

Next a BCF instruction is used to clear bit 5 of the Status register so that page 0 is selected. The next two lines then load a value of C1 into ADCON0, but this value appears as 0xC1 in the program listing. This is simply because some assemblers require the first digit in a hexadecimal value to be a number and not a letter, so that there is no risk of hexadecimal numbers being confused with labels or instructions. The 'sure fire' method of avoiding confusion when using the MPALC assembler is to use '0x' ahead of the hexadecimal digits. The value of C1 (11000001 in binary) written to ADCON0 performs three tasks. Firstly, by setting bit 0 to 1 the analogue to digital converter is switched on. Secondly, channel 0 is selected by setting bits 3 and 4 low. Finally, setting bits 6 and 7 high selects the internal C-R oscillator as the clock for the converter.

After this initial setting up the program moves into the loop that reads the converter and outputs the returned values on Port B. The BSF instruction sets bit 2 of ADCON0, and this starts the conversion. Note that this must always be done by a separate instruction, and not the one that is used to switch on the converter. The NOP instruction simply introduces a short delay to provide time for the conversion to be completed, but it might not be necessary in this case as the system clock is at a relatively low frequency in comparison to the converter's clock. The next two lines move the result of the conservation from the ADRES register to the W register, and then output the result to Port B. The program then loops back to the point where a conversion is initiated, and it keeps looping indefinitely, with readings being taken and written to Port B.

Basic Voltmeter

The next listing, together with the circuit diagram of Figure 5.8, uses the 16C71 to provide a basic digital voltmeter action. This

146

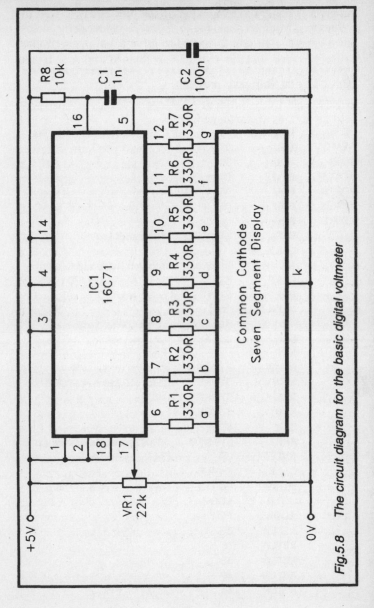

Fig.5.8   The circuit diagram for the basic digital voltmeter

147

program is really a combination of the previous two, with the values read from the analogue to digital converter being altered via a lookup table, and then used to drive a 7-segment display.

```
;************************************************
;Basic Digital Voltmeter program
;************************************************
;
PC          EQU     02
STATUS      EQU     03
BDIR        EQU     06
ADCON       EQU     08
PORTB       EQU     06
ADRES       EQU     09
STORE       EQU     0x0C
            BSF     STATUS,5    ;Select page 1
            CLRW
            MOVWF   BDIR        ;Sets Port B as outputs
            CLRF    ADCON       ;Sets RA0-RA3 as A/D inputs
            BCF     STATUS,5    ;Select page 0
            MOVLW   0xC1
            MOVWF   ADCON       ;Select Ch0/Int clock
LOOP        BSF     ADCON,2     ;Start conversion
            NOP                 ;Wait
            MOVF    ADRES,0     ;Place conversion in W
            MOVWF   STORE       ;Place conversion in STORE
            RRF     STORE,1
            RRF     STORE,1
            RRF     STORE,1
            RRF     STORE,0     ;Move high nibble into low nibble
            ANDLW   0F          ;Set high nibble to zero
            CALL    TABLE
            MOVWF   PORTB       ;Output conversion to Port B
            GOTO    LOOP
TABLE       ADDWF   PC,1
            RETLW   3F
            RETLW   06
            RETLW   5B
            RETLW   4F
            RETLW   66
```

148

```
RETLW    6D
RETLW    7D
RETLW    07
RETLW    7F
RETLW    6F
RETLW    77
RETLW    7C
RETLW    39
RETLW    5E
RETLW    79
RETLW    71
END
```

The initial part of the program is essentially the same as the beginning of the analogue to digital converter program, with the converter being set up for use with the internal C-R clock, and RA0 as the analogue input. Also as before, a conversion is started, the program waits briefly, and then the reading from the converter is started, the program waits briefly, and then reading from the converter is placed in the W register. The reading is then moved to a file register which acts as a temporary store, and a series of four rotate right (RRF) instructions are performed. The display can only handle 4-bit numbers, but the converter is producing 8-bit values. The most significant nibble could simply be masked off, with the least significant nibble being used to drive the display. However, accuracy is usually better if the most significant bits are used and the least significant bits are removed. The rotate right instructions shift the most significant nibble into bits 0 to 3 of the register, and the last of the four puts the result into the W register. The next instruction bitwise ANDs the contents of the W register with a masking number of 0F, which ensures that the most significant nibble is zero.

The lookup table subroutine is then called, and the appropriate value to drive the display is placed in the W register. This routine is much the same as the one used in the BCD to 7-segment decoder program described previously, but there are six more entries at the end of the lookup table. These produce the hexadecimal digits from 'A' to 'F', and the display therefore goes through the sixteen hexadecimal digits, from '0'

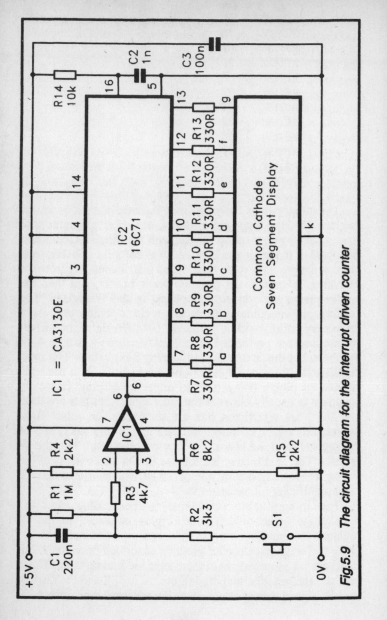

Fig.5.9 The circuit diagram for the interrupt driven counter

150

with VR1 set for minimum voltage, to 'F' with it set for maximum voltage. A 7-segment display is not designed to display letters of the alphabet, and a little artistic licence has to be used in order to get it to produce letters from 'A' to 'F'. The betters 'b' and 'd' are in lower case while the others are in upper case, but apart from this quite reasonable representations of the letters are produced.

Interrupts

The next program listing demonstrates the use of interrupts, and in conjunction with the circuit of Figure 5.9 it provides a basic counter action. The display starts at zero, but each time the pushbutton switch (S1) is operated the number on the display is incremented by one. The display is a hexadecimal type, and after the count reaches 'F' it cycles back to zero, and the counting process continues from there. Note that not all the PIC processors implement interrupts, and this feature is absent on the 16C54 for example.

```
;************************************************
;Interrupt demonstration program
;************************************************
;
PC        EQU     02
STATUS    EQU     03
BDIR      EQU     06
PORTB     EQU     06
CNTR      EQU     0C
STORE     EQU     0D
INTCN     EQU     0B
;
          GOTO    START       ;Jump over interrupt routine
          ORG     04          ;Set interrupt start address
          BCF     INTCN,1     ;Clear interrupt flag
          INCF    CNTR,1      ;Increment count
          RETFIE              ;Return from interrupt
;
START     CLRF    CNTR        ;Clear counter
          MOVLW   90
          MOVWF   INTCN       ;Enable interrupts on RB0
```

151

```
        BSF     STATUS,5    ;Select page 1
        MOVLW   01
        MOVWF   BDIR        ;Set RB1 to RB7 as outputs
        BCF     STATUS,5    ;Select page 0
LOOP    MOVF    CNTR,0      ;Load count into W register
        ANDLW   0F          ;Mask off top nibble
        CALL    TABLE       ;Convert 4 bit value to 7 bit code
        MOVWF   STORE       ;Move conversion into temporary
                              store
        RLF     STORE,0     ;Shift conversion left and place in
                              W
        MOVWF   PORTB       ;Output data to Port B
        GOTO    LOOP
TABLE   ADDWF   PC,1        ;Lookup table
        RETLW   3F
        RETLW   06
        RETLW   5B
        RETLW   4F
        RETLW   66
        RETLW   6D
        RETLW   7D
        RETLW   07
        RETLW   7F
        RETLW   6F
        RETLW   77
        RETLW   7C
        RETLW   39
        RETLW   5E
        RETLW   79
        RETLW   71
        END
```

The initial part of the listing assigns values to symbols, and then the program starts with a GOTO instruction. This may seem like an odd way to start the program, but it is jumping over the interrupt routine which is placed at the beginning of the program. The ORG instruction is not one in the PIC instruction set, as it is an assembler instruction, like EQU. It is the origin instruction, and it is telling the assembler to place the next instruction at address 04. The interrupt routine must therefore start at this address. All the interrupt routine does is to first reset the appropriate interrupt flag, and then increment the value stored in the register file used as the counter. The program then returns from the interrupt routine, the program counter is loaded from the Stack, and the program continues where it left off. Interrupts are automatically disabled while the interrupt routine is being performed, and they are automatically enabled by the RETFIE instruction when the program is returned to normal operation.

The section of the program from the 'START' label to the 'LOOP' label clears the register used as the counter, and then sets two bits in the interrupt control register (Figure 5.10). These are bits 7 and 4, which respectively enable global interrupts and interrupts on the INT pin (RB0 becomes the INT pin when interrupts are used). Note that interrupts are totally disabled when the global interrupt bit is at 0, and that just setting the interrupt bit for the type of interrupt you want to use is not sufficient. The global interrupt bit must be set, together with the bit or bits for the types of interrupts you wish to use. The rest of the START routine simply sets RB1 to RB7 as outputs, and these are used to drive the 7-segment display. It is not possible to drive the display from RB0 to RB6, as in the previous circuits that have used a 7-segment display, because RB0 is used as the interrupt input.

Once into the loop section, the program repeatedly loads the counter into the W register, gets the 4- to 7-bit conversion from the TABLE routine, and then outputs this value to the display. There is a minor complication here in that the display is not driven from the Port B lines used in our earlier examples, and the values needed to produce each digit are therefore different to those needed previously. A new set of lookup values could be calculated, but the easier option is to simply use the old values and shift the 7-bit codes one place to the left before outputting them to the display. This is the method used in this program.

In this simple demonstration program the main loop section of the program is not doing anything very worthwhile, and it is really just looping aimlessly waiting for an interrupt. In a real-world application the main loop would be doing something more worthwhile, and the interrupt routine would handle a task that needed instant attention when some external event

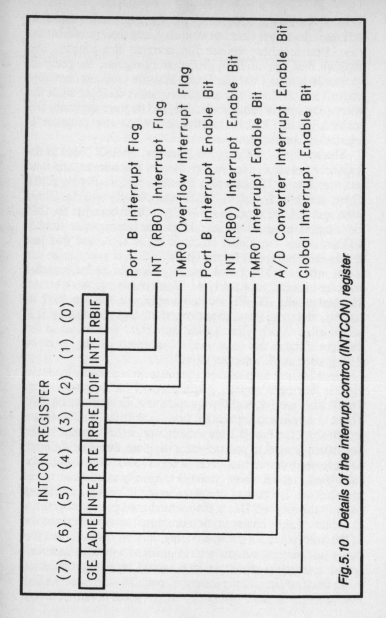

Fig.5.10 Details of the interrupt control (INTCON) register

INTCON REGISTER

(7) (6) (5) (4) (3) (2) (1) (0)

| GIE | ADIE | INTE | RTE | RBIE | TOIF | INTF | RBIF |

- Port B Interrupt Flag
- INT (RB0) Interrupt Flag
- TMR0 Overflow Interrupt Flag
- Port B Interrupt Enable Bit
- INT (RB0) Interrupt Enable Bit
- TMR0 Interrupt Enable Bit
- A/D Converter Interrupt Enable Bit
- Global Interrupt Enable Bit

occurred. Whenever using interrupts you need to make sure that the interrupt routine does not disturb the main program in any way. In this example the interrupt routine does not alter any registers that are used by the main program. In practical applications this will often occur though, and the interrupt routine must then store the data in any affected registers at the start of the routine, and restore the data to these registers just before returning from the interrupt. In most cases at least the W register will need to be saved and restored in this way.

When using external interrupts on the INT pin it is important to bear in mind that this input, in common with most interrupt inputs, is not tolerant of noise on the input signal, or slowly changing input levels. The result in either case is likely to be multiple operations of the interrupt routine. Mechanical switches are notorious for spurious output signals caused by so-called contact bounce, and this circuit therefore includes de-bouncing components (R1, R2, and C1) plus a trigger circuit based on IC1. This should give a 'clean' output signal that switches rapidly, which should in turn ensure that the count on the display only advances by one each time S1 is operated.

Note that the active transition on the INT input can be on the rising or falling edge of the input signal, depending on the setting of bit 6 in the OPTION register. Interrupts occur on the falling edge if this bit is set to 0, or the rising edge if it is set to 1. Bit 7 of the OPTION register also has a function in the 16C71. With this bit set to 0, the internal pull-up resistors on Port B are enabled, but they are disabled if this bit is set to 1. Figure 5.11 provides details of the 16C71 OPTION register.

The 16C71 supports three other sources of interrupts, which are TMR0, the analogue to digital converter, and Port B. TMR0 can generate an interrupt when it overflows, and the analogue to digital converter can produce one when it completes a conversion. An interrupt can also be generated by a change in the logic level on RB4 to RB7. The interrupt control register has bits which enable the four types of interrupt to be individually enabled or disabled, and in each case a bit is set to 1 to enable interrupts, and to 0 to disable them. There are also separate flags for each type of interrupt, and the appropriate flag must be cleared by the interrupt routine. The interrupt flag

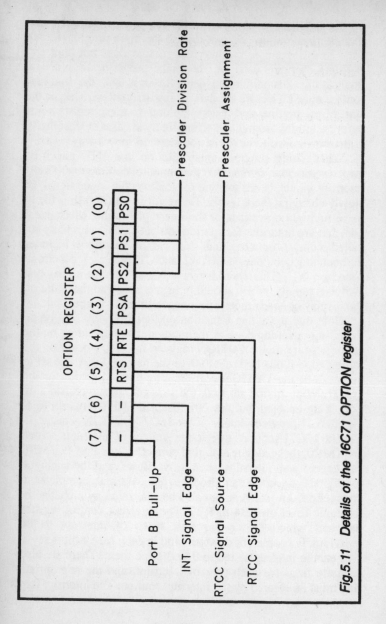

Fig.5.11 Details of the 16C71 OPTION register

for the analogue to digital converter is bit 1 of ADCON0, and it is not in the interrupt control register.

Using the RTCC

The circuit of Figure 5.12, in conjunction with the program provided here, acts as a simple seconds counter that utilizes the real-time clock counter (RTCC).

```
;**************************************************
;Seconds counter program using RTCC
;**************************************************
;
;
PORTB    EQU      06
CNTR     EQU      0A
RTCC     EQU      01
STATUS   EQU      03
Z        EQU      02
         CLRW
         TRIS     06          ;Sets B as outputs
         MOVLW    07
         OPTION               ;Selects system clock with /256
         MOVLW    3F
         MOVWF    PORTB       ;Sets display at zero initially
         CLRF     CNTR        ;Sets counter at zero
START    CLRF     RTCC        ;Sets RTCC at zero
         BCF      STATUS,Z    ;Clear zero flag
LOOP     MOVLW    0xFF        ;Load W with 11111111
         XORWF    RTCC,0      ;Checks to see if RTCC at max
         BTFSS    STATUS,Z    ;Loops until it is
         GOTO     LOOP
         INCF     CNTR,1      ;Increment counter
         MOVF     CNTR,0      ;Load W from counter
         CALL     TABLE       ;Load W from lookup table
         MOVWF    PORTB       ;Output number to Port B
         GOTO     START
         MOVWF    PORTB       ;Output data to Port B
         GOTO     START
TABLE    ADDWF    02,1        ;Lookup table
         RETLW    3F
         RETLW    06
```

157

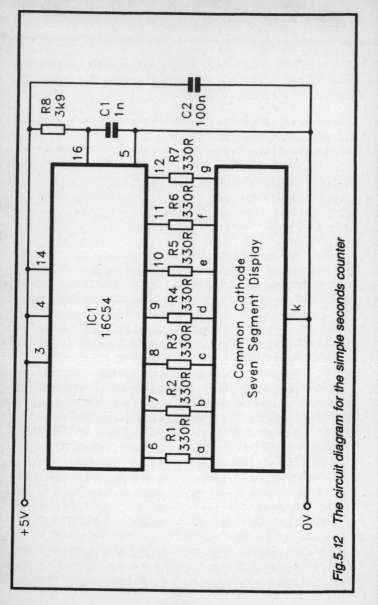

Fig.5.12 The circuit diagram for the simple seconds counter

```
RETLW     5B
RETLW     4F
RETLW     66
RETLW     6D
RETLW     7D
RETLW     07
RETLW     7F
RETLW     6F
RETLW     77
RETLW     7C
RETLW     39
RETLW     5E
RETLW     79
RETLW     71
END
```

Much of the program follows along the same lines as previous examples, and we will therefore concentrate on the sections that deal with the real-time clock. The counter can use the divided by four system clock or external pulses on the RTCC pin as its signal source. In this case we require the system clock as the pulse source, and bit 5 of the OPTION register must be set to 0. We will be using the prescaler with a division rate of 256, which requires bits 0 to 2 of the OPTION register to be set to 1. A value of 07 is therefore written to the OPTION register. the RTCC register is cleared, the zero flag is also cleared, and a value of FF (11111111 in binary) is loaded into the W register. The value in the RTCC register is then bitwise XORed with the value in the W register, and the result is placed in the W register. This provides the complement of the value in RTCC, which will be zero only once the maximum count has been reached. The zero flag is tested, and the program loops until this flag has been set (i.e. it loops until the RTCC register reaches its maximum count). The register containing the number to be displayed is then incremented, the appropriate 7-bit value is obtained from the lookup table, and so on.

The specified values in the C-R clock circuit result in the count incrementing at approximately one second intervals. In order to obtain precise counting it would be necessary to use a

crystal clock circuit and to experiment a little with the delay
loop in order to optimise results.

Two Digits

This program, together with the circuit of Figure 5.13, acts as a
simple 2-digit seconds counter. It requires a 16C55 so that the
least significant digit can be driven from Port B, and the most
significant digit can be driven from Port C.

```
;**************************************************
;TWO DIGIT COUNTER PROGRAM
;LEAST SIGNIFICANT DIGIT ON RB0 TO RB6
;MOST SIGNIFICANT DIGIT ON RC0 TO RC6
;**************************************************
;
STATUS   EQU      03
Z        EQU      02
LNIBL    EQU      0A
HNIBL    EQU      0B
CNTR     EQU      0E
PORTB    EQU      06
PORTC    EQU      07
PC       EQU      02
MOVLW    0xFF
         MOVWF    CNTR       ;Load FF in delay counter
         CLRW
         TRIS     06         ;Set Port B as outputs
         TRIS     07         ;Set Port C as outputs
START    CLRF     LNIBL
         CLRF     HNIBL
LOOP     MOVF     LNIBL,W
         BCF      STATUS,Z
         XORLW    0A
         BTFSC    STATUS,Z   ;Check if low nibble reached 10
         CALL     PLUSH      ;Zero and INC high nibble if it is
         MOVF     LNIBL,W
         CALL     TABLE
         MOVWF    PORTB
         MOV      HNIBL,W
         BCF      STATUS,Z
```

160

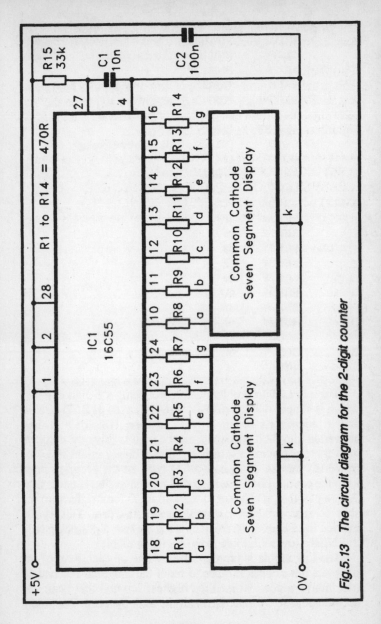

Fig.5.13 The circuit diagram for the 2-digit counter

161

```
          XORLW      0A
          BTFSC      STATUS,Z   ;Check if high nibble reached 10
          CLRF       HNIBL      ;Reset nibble if it has
          MOVF       HNIBL,W
          CALL       TABLE      ;Load W with display data
          MOVWF      PORTC      ;Output data to Port C
          INCF       LNIBL,1    ;Increment counter
DELAY     DECFSZ     CNTR
          GOTO       DELAY      ;Delay before looping
          GOTO       LOOP
PLUSH     INCF       HNIBL
          CLRF       LNIBL
TABLE     ADDWF      PC,1
          RETLW      3F
          RETLW      06
          RETLW      5B
          RETLW      4F
          RETLW      66
          RETLW      6D
          RETLW      7D
          RETLW      07
          RETLW      7F
          RETLW      6F
          END
```

There is a slight problem when producing a 2-digit counter, which is simply that the display is really a type of BCD circuit, and it requires its raw data in BCD form. This data is then converted into 7-bit codes that can be used to drive the displays with the right numbers. Either a direct binary count must be converted into an equivalent BCD type, or the program must keep the count in BCD form so that no conversion is necessary. Where possible, it is better to work in BCD form right from the start so that complex conversions are avoided. This is the method used here, with the counts for the two digits being held in LNIBL (low nibble) and HNIBL (high nibble).

The low nibble is incremented by one on each loop of the program, but a check is made to see if the count has reached 10 (decimal), since 9 is the highest count that can be accommodated by one BCD digit, and by each 7-segment display. The low nibble is XORed with a hexadecimal value of 0A (equivalent to 10 in decimal), and this gives a result of zero only if the count is at 0A. If a value of 0A is detected, the low nibble is reset to zero and the high nibble is incremented. A check has to be kept on the value in the high nibble as well, because this must not exceed 9 either. This is achieved using basically the same routine, and when a value of 0A is detected the high nibble is reset to zero. There is no third digit, and once the count has reached '99' the count and the display go back to '00' and start counting up once again.

It would be possible to extend the count to more digits, but it would be necessary to use multiplexing techniques. This is the only way to provide enough outputs to drive more than two digits. Even with just a 2-digit display, a 16C55 is needed to provide the fourteen outputs that are needed. Another file register would be allocated to the value for the third digit, and this would be incremented each time the second digit was reset to zero. The third digit would, like the other two, have to be reset to zero when the count reached 0A. If the second digit was reset when a count of six was reached, the display would count in minutes and seconds. One of the main advantages of using microcontrollers is that the system is easily adapted to handle this type of thing. It is often possible to find software solutions rather than having to add extra hardware.

Finally
Before trying to produce 'proper' PIC projects it is a good idea to make some experiments with simple programs. Try writing routines to drive 7-segment displays, detect when the analogue input is between certain voltages, and things of this type. This will build up valuable experience which will help you to write the software for real world applications. You will also build up a library of useful routines that can be modified for use in 'real' programs.

Appendix 1

ELECTRICAL RATINGS

These are the supply voltage ranges for PIC microcontrollers.

Device Type	Min Supply V	Max Supply V
XT	3.25	6.25
RC	3.25	6.25
HS	4.5	5.5
LP	2.5	6.25

Note that in the LP, RC, and XT modes the 16C71 should be used with a supply potential in the range 4.0 to 6.0 volts.

Provided a 5 volt supply is used, the digital inputs and outputs of the PIC processors are compatible with TTL devices, and they also seem to interface with CMOS logic devices reliably. It is possible for an output to source currents of up to 20 milliamps, and sink currents of up to 25 milliamps. However, the maximum source and sink currents per port are 40 and 50 milliamps respectively, and this would normally be the limiting factor.

The supply current depends on the type of device and its operating frequency. For XT and RC devices operating with a clock frequency of 4MHz, the typical current consumption is just 1.8 milliamps (3.3 milliamps maximum). The consumption for an HS device operating at 20MHz is 9.0 milliamps (20 milliamps maximum). Operation at lower frequencies gives reduced operating current, and the typical current consumption at 100kHz is a little under 100 microamps. An LP device operating with a 32kHz clock typically consumes just 15 microamps (32 microamps maximum). Bear in mind that these figures are for the current consumption of the chip itself, and do not take into account any output currents to displays, relay drivers, etc. If the chip is used to drive three or four 7-segment displays the current consumption will obviously be many times higher. When a device is in the SLEEP mode the current consumption is typically just 4 microamps with the watchdog timer enabled, or 0.6 microamps (9 microamps maximum) with it switched off. The analogue to digital converter of the 16C71 consumes about 90 microamps when enabled, and does not significantly increase the supply current when it is switched off.